THE
PERFECT
CORNER
2

THE
PERFECT
CORNER
2

A Driver's
STEP-BY-STEP GUIDE
to Optimizing
COMPLEX SECTIONS
Through the
PHYSICS OF RACING

The Science of Speed Series

created by PARADIGM SHIFT DRIVER DEVELOPMENT
written by ADAM BROUILLARD

PARADIGM·SHIFT
DRIVER DEVELOPMENT

www.paradigmshiftracing.com

ISBN-13: 978-0-9973824-4-0
ISBN-10: 0-9973824-4-9

Published by Paradigm Shift Motorsport Books
The Perfect Corner 2 and The Science of Speed Series
are trademarks of Paradigm Shift Driver Development.

www.paradigmshiftracing.com

For information about custom editions, special
sales, premium and corporate purchases please
contact:

Paradigm Shift Driver Development
development@paradigmshiftracing.com
470.240.1582.

CONTENTS

"If you can't explain it simply, you don't understand it well enough."

- Albert Einstein

BEYOND THE **STANDARD CORNER**

While the basic principles of Line Theory that we learned in *The Perfect Corner* will take you far, there are some unique track situations that take special rules. While the eventual answer is not any harder to execute than a standard corner, how we get there can be a little complex. This will be worth the effort however, because while trial and error will often eventually lead you to at least close to the right answer with standard corners, understanding how Line Theory works in more complex track sections can give you a significant advantage. Even in the higher levels of motorsport, some drivers misunderstand how to optimize complex track sections and will debate various ways to handle them. Being able to quickly determine how to optimize a complex section can be a great benefit and we can do this with just a few new rules.

We'll start out with a summary of basic Line Theory and then we will push your understanding of its rules to the limit. Next, we will look at the new rules needed when combining corners, as well as the surprising science of optimizing straights. Finally, we will end by breaking down some of the most complex corner sequences in the world. If you can learn how to solve these puzzling track sections, you will be able to figure out how to drive anything.

You can also be assured that these rules provide a complete solution. They work with virtually every vehicle, on any track. You sometimes hear discussion about which corner on the track is most important or the concept of grading corners, but while certain corners will certainly have greater potential to change your lap times, this doesn't affect how you should drive them. There is time to be gained and lost in every corner and you can use the same principles to optimize them all.

STANDARD **LINE THEORY** SUMMARIZED

To get started, let's lay out a basic summary of everything we learned about Line Theory so far in *The Perfect Corner*.

- A driver should set their braking point based on how their entry spiral carries them to the apex. If their spiral does not reach the apex, they need an earlier braking point. If their spiral would carry them off the inside of the track, they need a later braking point.

- Once the driver starts turning into their entry spiral, they will try to reduce their radius as quickly as possible by maximizing their tire forces pushing them in the ideal direction. The pre-apex ideal direction is basically at the same angle as the track during corner entry.

- An entry spiral's starting speed determines its size and therefore where in the corner it needs to start. For a given corner, a larger, faster, and earlier starting spiral will create an earlier apex. A smaller, slower starting spiral will create a later apex, but will need to start later.

- With an earlier apex, the vehicle will be at a higher speed and will have turned less as it passes by. A later apex will have a lower apex speed and the vehicle will have turned more as it passes.

- The shape of the inside of the corner will determine the exact location of the apex. This will create a steady progression of a certain speed and angle attainable as the apex moves from earlier to later along the inside of the track.

- As they pass the apex, the driver will maximize the vehicle's acceleration in the ideal direction. The post-apex ideal direction will be in the same direction as the track exit.

- If maximum acceleration would carry the vehicle off track, the driver needs a later, slower apex. If there is space left at trackout, the driver will need an earlier, faster apex. This new apex will require a different spiral and thus a different braking point.

But are there no exceptions? What about off-road driving? What about racing on a wet track? What about elevation changes and banking? These situations don't actually change the rules, but they will test how well you understand them. As an example, while racing in the rain, it is often standard practice to avoid driving on the standard line if on a well-worn track where the racing line is very slippery when wet. If the grip on the standard line is only half what driving off the line produces then this will just effectively change where the edges of the track are. Those curbs are no longer the edge of the track. Now the edge is where the track grip level significantly changes and you must use Line Theory principles to optimize around these new track limits. If you used your car control abilities to find this area of high grip, you might discover that now your apex is out in the middle of the track or it could even turn a standard corner into a double apex. You still want to maximize your movement in the ideal direction before and after the apex, but the results are completely different now from when the track was dry.

Often the best line for an off-road motorcycle is wherever the rut has formed.

Changes in track geometry work the same way. Off-camber corners, high banking, crests, dips. They might change the grip you have at any moment, but the rules stay the same. For example, consider a corner that is off-camber near the apex and then transitions to have some banking near the corner exit. A car would gain extra force production capacity (grip) as it progressed through its acceleration arc. This would change its lateral vs longitudinal force generating capability to be as if it was a less powerful car. So just like a less powerful car, this would create a more circular acceleration arc, but only for that specific corner. A driver goes through this same line finding process on every corner however. Different cars, setups, pavement grip levels, track geometry, weather. These will all create a unique solution each time. The process and the rules however, will always be the same.

Beyond just modifying a line, track geometry can also progressively change the efficiency of different lines and minimize or magnify mistakes. For example, a well-designed curb will cause a car to progressively lose grip the farther off track it drives. The more curb used however, the more ideal the line so there can be a range of lines where using more and more curb won't change lap times very much. A well marbled track causes the opposite to happen where a car progressively loses grip the further off line and into the marbles it drives.

Bristol Motor Speedway has actually used track geometry on purpose to promote close racing. The track has a progressive banking where the higher line is more angled. This evens out the efficiency of multiple lines to make passing easier. Sometimes track geometry can even be so extreme however, that the best line might be completely different from what the ideal line would normally be. Often the best line through a corner for an off-road motorcycle is wherever the rut has formed. The force generating potential in the rut is so much higher that it could be far from a normal ideal line for a fresh track, but still be faster.

Bristol Motor Speedway's progressive banking promotes close racing by increasing the efficiency of alternate lines.

LINE THEORY TESTED

Whether it was the track designer's intention or not, a racetrack will sometimes fool you. The track edges can be a red herring. As we move beyond standard corners, you'll learn how the key to navigating complex sections is often to find the real limits of the track. To visualize your own perfect racetrack within the real track and optimize around the ideal points, which are not necessarily always the track edges.

Before we get to complex sections however, we are going to first deepen our understanding of basic Line Theory. We are going to put it to the test. We're going to try to break it. Doing thought experiments like these can be a really good exercise to help you understand the physics of racing and how you can apply it in any situation.

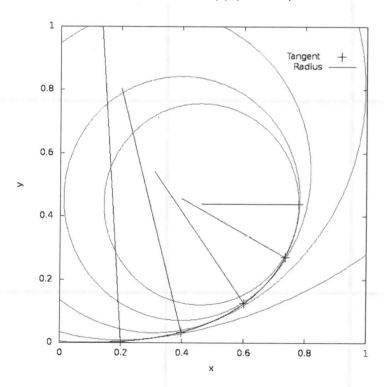

You might recognize this graph from the end of *The Perfect Corner*. It shows how the Euler spiral is essentially made of a series of smaller and smaller circles as you travel along the path. We are going to use this illustration for this first section, as it will allow us to have an exact measure of how our apex speed and angle will change as we move along the spiral.

A **STANDARD** CORNER

Let's start with a basic corner made of two track edges and a cone for an apex. This would mimic a standard road course corner. We've laid out the spiral to show how you would optimize this configuration. You can easily identify the corner entry ideal direction in this section, as it will be parallel to the graph. The entry spiral starts at the exact same angle as the graph edge at the bottom. Because this corner is optimized, it is also at the same angle as the track edge.

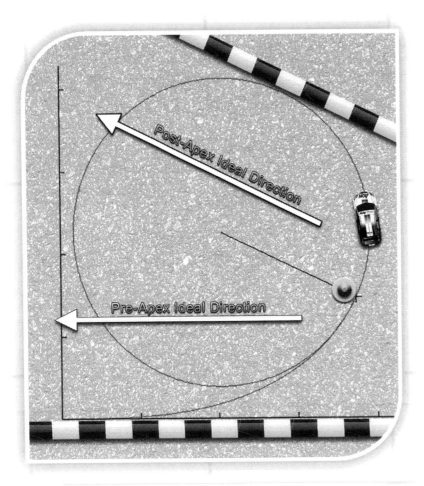

The size of the circle shows the maximum speed the car could attain at the apex. This example car will maintain this speed throughout the rest of the corner at full throttle. This is not completely realistic, but is quite close to reality for lower-powered cars and will help to visualize how the attainable apex speed will reduce as the circle shrinks while the car moves along the spiral with a later and slower apex.

The corner ends when the circle meets the track edge. Here that is 90 degrees from the apex and the car would continue straight at this point along the track edge. The corner exit ideal direction is therefore at the same angle as the track edge.

A **STANDARD** CORNER (**HIGH-ACCELERATION**)

Now let's look at how this same corner would look with a car having the same maximum grip potential, but more power to accelerate. We have flipped and copied the Euler spiral so the corner exit path will have an increasing radius that mirrors the corner entry. This would be the idealized path the astronaut would travel on and only a high-powered 4-wheel drive car would ideally drive this line. A high-acceleration rear-wheel drive car in a slow corner could come very close however.

Notice how the ideal directions are still the same as previously and follow the track edges. The ideal direction would be parallel to the angle the car starts and ends the corner. This is determined by the track edge, not the acceleration potential of the car.

The high-power car is able to accelerate in the post-apex ideal direction more effectively than the slower car, but will require a later, slower apex to accomplish this. The high-power car will take slightly longer to get to its apex, but will complete the entire corner much faster.

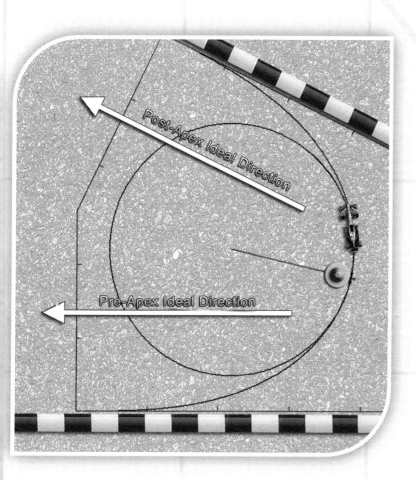

LOW VS **HIGH** ACCELERATION

Here we have overlaid our previous two illustrations. The thicker dark line shows the high-acceleration car. Both apexes are basically at the same point at the cone, but the higher acceleration car has a later and slower apex. You can see that the apex speed is slower because the circle is smaller and the angle of the radius line shows that it has also turned more by the apex. The car with greater acceleration would need this slower, later apex to better use its power during corner exit.

It's useful to note that the lines are quite close to each other, especially at corner entry. Practically every car from a super high-powered F1 car to a low-powered stock autocross car would travel somewhere between these two lines. The speeds could be very different, but the paths of travel are fairly close. The biggest difference is where the car hits the track edge at corner exit and as we start to mix things up, that difference is going to become important.

This should all just be a review so far, but we wanted to make sure you're up to speed if it has been awhile since reading *The Perfect Corner*.

SETTING YOUR OWN **IDEAL DIRECTION**

Let's now remove the curbs and replace them with cones. On a normal racetrack, your ideal direction is usually easy to visualize and follow because it will basically be the same direction as the edge of the track. When you are only limited by a single point as with a cone however, you can decide your own direction of travel as you pass it, and thus your own ideal direction. So let's see how we go about optimizing a corner when we have this freedom to choose how we approach and leave it.

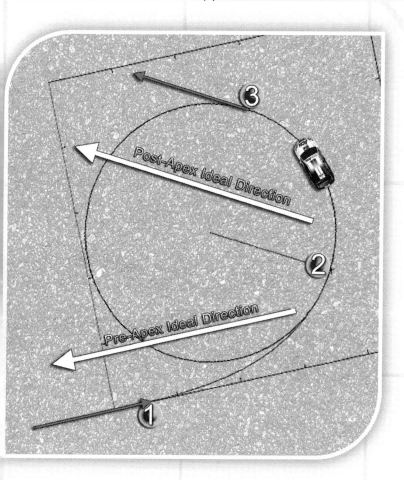

Because we aren't limited by the track edge, we can pass the 1st cone at a greater angle than the curb was allowing. This angles out our pre-apex ideal direction and allows a slightly faster corner entry.

The corner exit however, looks identical to before as the placement of the 3rd cone makes this low-powered car still have a 90-degree corner exit. Having freedom to choose your own ideal directions won't always necessarily allow you to complete a corner faster. It depends on the cone placement, but also on the car capabilities. So let's see how the high-acceleration car would optimize this.

Well this looks quite different. When we put a car with greater acceleration potential through these cones, the ideal directions can be spread out even more. Because the track edge is now only a single point, we can take advantage of the extra angle allowed and carry more speed into and out of the corner. Although this requires a slower apex speed, (the circle is smaller), our overall elapsed time would be lower and our entry and exit speed would be higher.

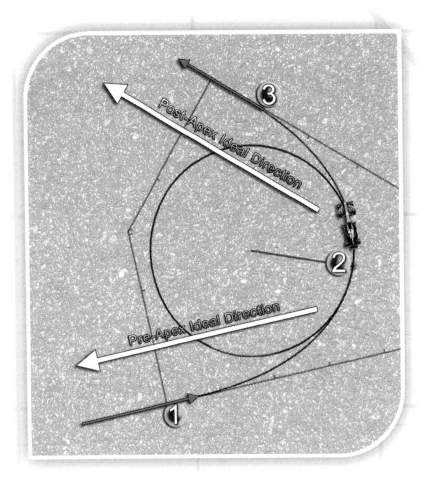

The reason for this is related to how we set our ideal directions in relation to the track edge. This is something you might not notice when you have a normal track edge, but here you can see how the entry spiral starts at the 1st cone and the acceleration arc ends right at the 3rd. That is not a coincidence.

While this relationship is easy to visualize with cones, each and every corner is made up of just 3 points. Even on a normal track with no cones, if we can find the best 3 points to optimize, we can make our own perfect corner.

FOLLOW THE **CONES**

Let's see what happens now when we move the 1st cone closer to the apex. You'll notice how our entry spiral has followed the cone and this causes our ideal direction to move further out. This allows us to carry even more speed closer to the apex because we have more angle to work with. Notice also we've moved back to our low-powered car with a circular exit that goes 90 degrees. Because the 2nd and 3rd cone is the same as before, the exit is exactly the same as well (the apex speed and angle is the same), although we have been able to increase our entry speed and reach that apex much faster.

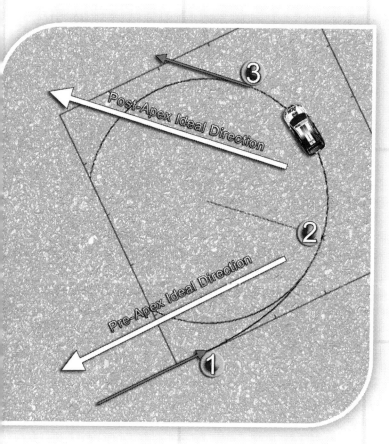

Our goal here is not to spread out the ideal directions as much as possible however. If we wanted to, we could drive past the 1st cone at even more of an angle and do an even tighter entry spiral. This would move our ideal direction further out, but it would compromise our apex and make it slower.

Instead, our goal is to generate as much force as possible pushing us in the ideal direction. To accomplish this, we want to use as much of the spiral as possible, but only up to a certain limit. We've mentioned it a few times, but now we'll learn more about the significance of this 90-degree limit.

THE **90-DEGREE LIMIT**

Let's now look at what happens when we move the 2nd cone closer to the 3rd so we have a really tight corner exit compared to the entry. If we started our entry spiral right at the 1st cone as we did previously, we now run wide and can't make our 3rd cone unless we lifted off the throttle. This is because we are only using the first 90 degrees of the Euler spiral as we have been doing so far.

That certainly is a problem, so what do we do here? Why exactly have we never gone beyond 90 degrees in either our entry spiral or during our acceleration arc before? To find out, let's try trail braking longer to the apex by going further in the spiral and see what happens.

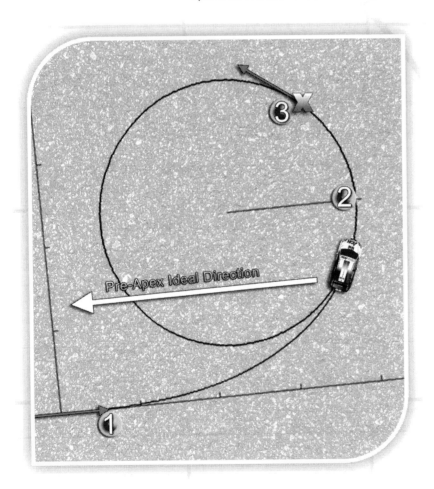

THE **PROBLEM** WITH A **LONG SPIRAL**

Okay, this looks pretty good. We're trail braking all the way to the apex and we've made the 3rd cone now. If a skilled driver did a corner in this way however, something wouldn't feel quite right.

You'll notice in the illustration how we no longer have our corner entry ideal direction marked. Usually our ideal direction is parallel to the graph and the spiral start direction.

We can't do that here however, because as the driver entered the corner and passed the 1st cone, they would start their entry spiral as usual, but as they approached the apex and reached the 90-degree point, they would notice a problem.

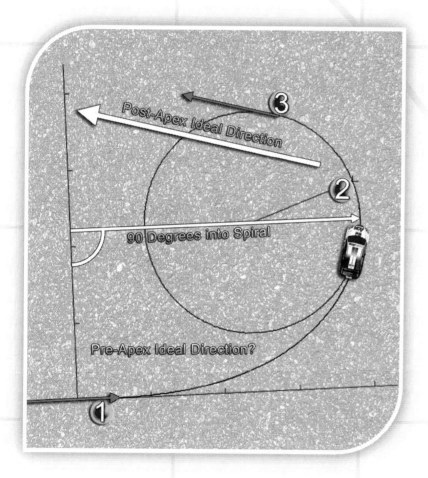

The crossed arrows in this illustration show the problem. The dark arrow shows the ideal direction at the beginning of the spiral and the white arrow shows it at the apex. The overlapping arrow directions are an issue because by the time the driver hits the apex, they have cancelled out some of the forces they generated earlier in the entry spiral. The entry will then be unnecessarily longer than something a shorter, more optimal line will accomplish. If you ever pass 90 degrees during entry and still haven't reached the apex, this is exactly what is happening.

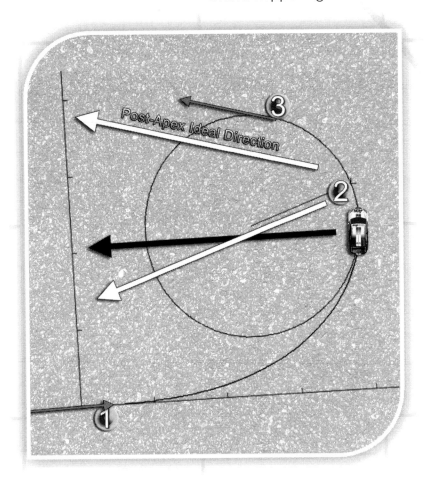

A good driver will notice this problem because the ideal direction they set when they enter the spiral only works up to 90 degrees. Once the car has turned to the point that their ideal direction is now directly sideways as in this illustration, continuing to trail brake won't help move them in the ideal direction anymore.

All they can do is continue at neutral throttle until they reach the apex and can start accelerating. This steady state turning will feel slow to the driver, and they'll know they've made a mistake. As we'll see soon, there will be situations similar to this that aren't a mistake, but never on a single apex.

This illustration shows how a driver will need to properly optimize this cone configuration. They will brake in a straight line past the 1st cone and this straight-line braking meets up with the beginning of their entry spiral. Then they will use 90 degrees of the spiral, but no more. Again, using more than 90 degrees causes the tire forces you generate to work against themselves and this will make your line unnecessarily long.

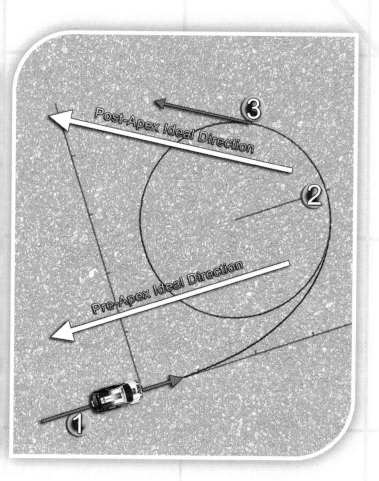

You do want to use as much up to 90 degrees as you can fit in the corner however. The more spiral you use, the faster your apex speed can be without compromising your entry. As in this configuration, sometimes this 90-degree limit might require you to initiate your entry spiral out in the middle of the track, and not next to the edge.

While this type of corner configuration sometimes occurs in autocross, in road course racing, having to straight-line brake away from the track edge before turn-in is not common. It would usually require a wide track on entry that became much narrower during the exit. Most road courses have a pretty consistent track width so you rarely encounter something like this during a standard corner. You still need to understand this 90-degree limit however, because…

LINE THEORY BROKEN?

You will run into corners like this. Oak Tree at VIR is a corner that looks like it will require more than 90 degrees to get to the apex, but this illustration shows how using up all 90 degrees isn't going to work. You wouldn't be able to carry the necessary speed and angle to the beginning of the spiral so straight-line braking at an angle away from the track edge just won't work. Many drivers struggle with corners like this because, although there are many ways to drive through it, there is only one optimal way.

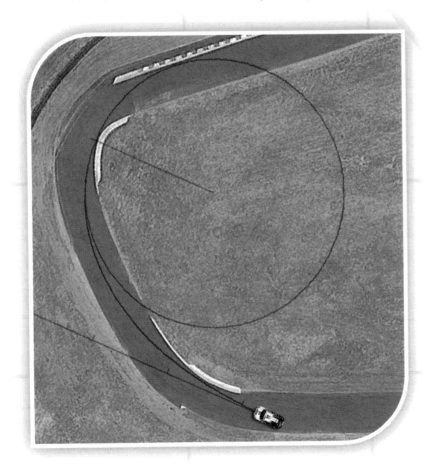

Our standard Line Theory rules we have learned so far aren't going to get us there however. To optimize this corner we are going to have to dig a little deeper because we have just ran into...

A **Double Apex**.

A 4ᵀᴴ CONE (**DOUBLE APEXES**)

Let's take a step back now so we can work through this one step at a time. To tackle the double apex you have to understand that now you essentially have four cones (points) to deal with and optimize

First however, when dealing with a suspected double apex, it's a good idea to check and see if it truly is a double apex. Sometimes it may not be and if you can optimize it with standard Line Theory rules, that is definitely the way to go. Just because some might call a corner a double apex doesn't mean it necessarily is one.

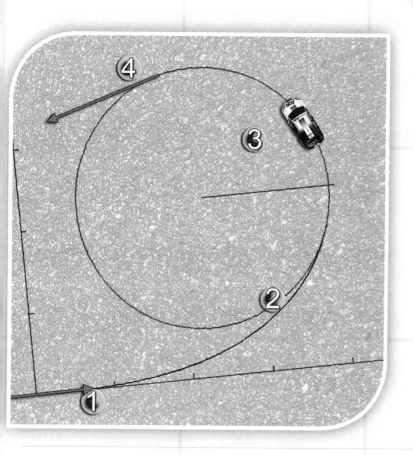

Sometimes a corner that looks like a double apex actually isn't and sometimes one that is a double apex in one type of car isn't in another. To find out if a corner can be optimized with standard rules, you will need to see if you can find a single apex that will allow both an optimal entry and exit. In this illustration, our driver has attempted to drive an entry spiral all the way to the 3ʳᵈ cone and just can't get there staying under the 90-degree limit. So trail braking to that cone isn't going to work and this might be a double apex. There is one other thing we can try however.

We can try optimizing the 2nd cone as an apex instead. This actually doesn't look too bad, but again we have a problem. You'll notice we've gone nearly 180 degrees in our acceleration arc to reach the 4th cone after we pass the apex. Just as during corner entry, we shouldn't ever go past 90 degrees during corner exit either. This makes our line unnecessarily longer and slower than a more optimized solution.

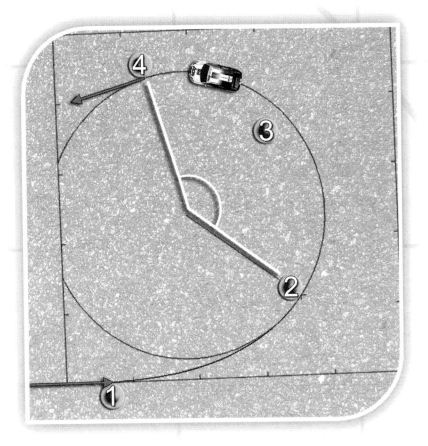

As neither of our two possible apex cones worked without breaking the 90-degree limit, it does seem like we truly are dealing with a double apex. At least with this low-acceleration car.

Before jumping straight into our double apex technique however, let's try this again using our high-acceleration car and see if maybe that will change things.

Going to the other end of the spectrum with a high-acceleration car looks to be even worse and shows how you will typically identify a double apex. We aren't just cancelling out forces now, we can't even make the corner. Again, with a double apex, you will be unable to find a single apex where you can optimize the entry **and** the exit without going past 90 degrees on either.

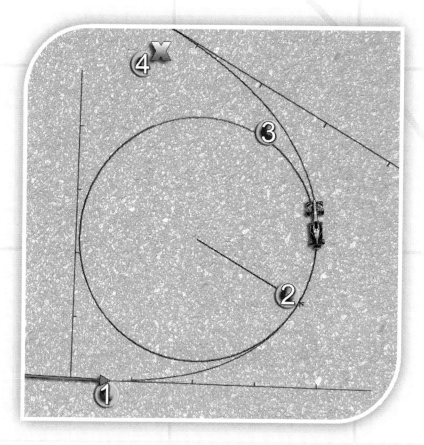

A double apex is typically created when two corners going in the same direction are close together. We'll also see how other types of corners that look nothing like a typical double apex will need to be optimized as one however.

We'll further look at how understanding the way to optimize a double apex even helps you to correct mistakes in standard single apex corners.

We'll get to all of that soon, but first we want to point out that...

This is not a double apex. Just because you pass more than three points as you negotiate a corner does not mean a corner is a double apex. We've moved the cones so this illustration shows a standard corner where the 2nd cone is right next to the path of the car. The key here is that the 2nd cone does not compromise the driver's line any, so it is not an apex.

This may seem somewhat obvious, but many corners on a racetrack are very close to possibly being either a standard corner or a double apex because there is a point on the inside of the track that only compromises a car's line very little or not at all depending on the situation.

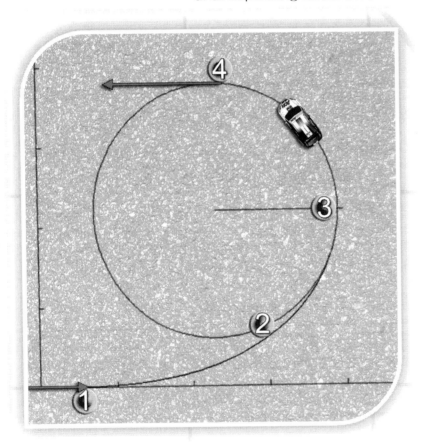

Even a very skilled and consistent driver that had little variability in their driving might change how they need to optimize the corner sometimes. In this illustration for example, if the driver over-slowed their entry even a little, they actually would need to treat this as a double apex and we'll learn why shortly. First though, let's see how we go about working up a basic double apex so we can build our knowledge from there.

OPTIMIZING THE 1ST APEX

Now back with our original 4-cone configuration, if you discover you truly are dealing with a double apex, you'll need to optimize for it. Rather than just show you the answer, let's work through this the way a driver would.

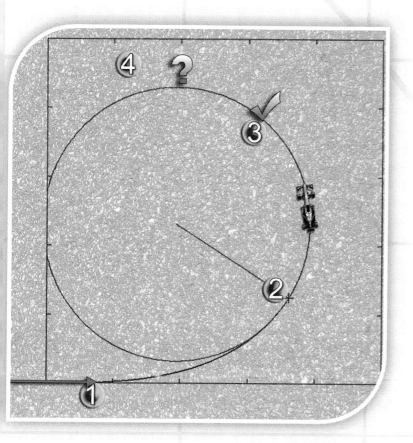

The first step would be to set an entry spiral to the 1st apex at cone 2 as you would with a standard corner. This time however, you'll want to plan close to a circular exit path to the 2nd apex at cone 3. You are **not** trying to maximize acceleration after the 1st apex as you would in a standard corner. Right now your goal is to just make it to the 2nd apex while driving at the limit.

Also, as with any corner, it's important to remember this is just a prediction at this point. We won't know how optimal this is until the corner is over.

OPTIMIZING THE **2ND APEX**

As your circular path passes the 2nd apex, you will begin your acceleration arc. If you can then achieve an optimal corner exit to cone 4, you'll know your prediction at the 1st apex was good. We got lucky this time as our corner entry and then a constant circle between the two apexes yielded an ideal corner exit.

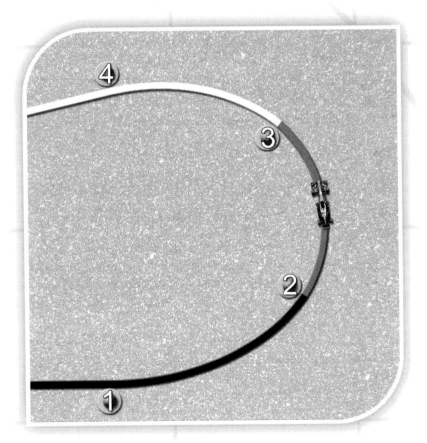

The dark line shows our standard entry spiral and the white line shows our standard maximum acceleration exit, but the grey line shows a circular path between the two apexes. That definitely doesn't fit within our standard Line Theory rules. So what's going on here?

A double apex is a unique situation where maximizing force to move the car in a singular ideal direction is no longer the goal. The standard rules of Line Theory allow us to minimize lap times because standard corners are completely separate from each other. One corner does not directly affect how you optimize the next. While a change in performance in one corner may affect where your braking point is or how deep you go into the entry spiral before you begin decelerating, it does not affect your optimal apex and line. That is set by the geometry of the corner and the car's capabilities. Having a corner be completely independent allows us to use the entire track width to increase entry and exit speed, and therefore lower our times.

> Drive between the two apexes in the shortest distance possible that allows an optimal entry and exit.

But when you have two corners close together as in a double apex, the more you optimize one apex, the less optimized the other becomes. This puts us in a sort of apex limbo where our primary goal now becomes not about maximizing the direction of force, but about efficiency.

Although the massive oak tree at VIR fell in 2013, the corner's namesake lives on in the hearts and minds of racers.

A **CIRCULAR** RACETRACK

The easiest way to understand what is going on here is to picture how you would drive around a circular racetrack. You could increase your speed in one particular section by going out wider, slowing down, and then coming back in at a faster speed. This is essentially what we are doing when we optimize a standard corner, but in the case of a circular racetrack, it should hopefully be obvious this would simply increase our lap

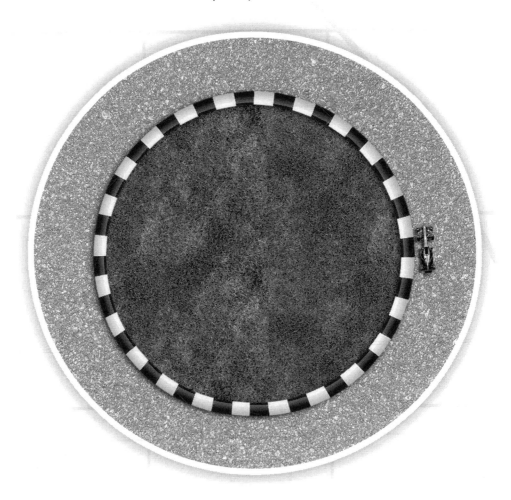

times. Anything other than just driving around the inside of the track on the shortest line possible would be slower than optimal because it's less efficient. There are no straightaways that separate corners and allow us to use the width of the track to increase entry and exit speed. For a circular track, the answer is simply to take the shortest path possible and this principle shows us how to do a double apex.

If it's not intuitive that the shortest path is the fastest, you might be thinking, "Well if I drive on a bigger circle, I can drive faster so would it not just even out and end up producing the same lap times?" While you can drive faster on a bigger circle, it is not a linear relationship, it is actually a squared one. As an example, to drive around a 200-meter circle in the same time it takes to drive around a 100-meter circle in a car that has 1 g of maximum grip, you would need to drive at twice the speed. To accomplish this greater speed however, you would need to have a car capable of generating 2 g. Double what this one can produce. As mentioned at the beginning of the book, this is why the banking at Bristol needs to progressively increase in angle to even out the different line efficiencies. The shorter line is inherently more efficient.

So if our goal now is to maximize efficiency, how can we ensure we are accomplishing that? Do we always just drive on a circular path between the two apexes? Not always. While that was the solution in our first example, it was just the answer in that one situation. Just like with the circular racetrack, your goal is to drive the shortest distance possible, but we also need a path that allows an optimal entry and exit. So let's see if we can figure out an efficient way to move through this apex limbo while also not compromising our entry and exit.

CONNECTED APEXES

Figuring out this ideal path is not as complicated as it may seem because the way we drive the first apex directly affects how we pass the second if driven properly. Their angles are connected. The earlier and faster you the pass the first apex, the later and slower you will pass the second, and vice versa.

This illustration shows our previous example except this time the driver has apexed earlier and thus faster on the 1st apex. In order to then make it to the 2nd apex, the driver must continue to slow down and turn more than before. This causes them to pass the 2nd apex later and slower than our previous optimal solution and leaves a lot of unused track width left at corner exit.

It's important to note that in this example, the driver is not reducing their radius as fast as possible between the two apexes as they were before the 1st apex. They would still be at the limit, but they are only reducing their radius just enough to make their path meet the 2nd apex.

Exit Too Late and Slow
=
Entry Too Early and Fast

In this illustration now, the driver has passed the 1st apex later and therefore slower than optimal. Again, they are still at the limit between the two apexes, but this time they will be accelerating just enough that their path will meet the 2nd apex. They will now pass the 2nd apex earlier and faster than optimal. This would cause them to miss cone 4 if they continued with their normal acceleration arc. Now of course, the driver could recognize this mistake earlier and still make the corner, but just as with a standard corner, any mistake leading up to the 1st apex is going to cause an unavoidable lap time penalty. While it's easy to tell from these illustrations how the apex angles are linked, this only works if you drive in the proper way between the two apexes.

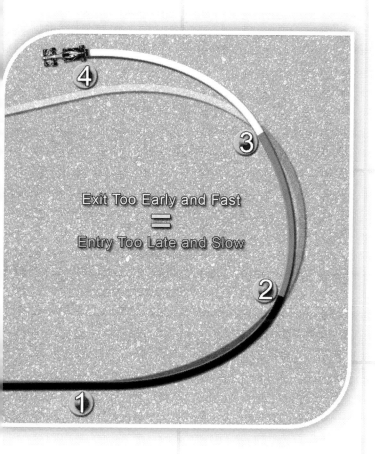

Exit Too Early and Fast
=
Entry Too Late and Slow

In this illustration for example, instead of accelerating just a little bit to get to the 2nd apex, the driver could have started accelerating hard after the 1st apex gaining speed just like they would in a standard corner exit. This would cause them to then need to decelerate and reduce radius somewhere in the middle to reach the 2nd apex.

The driver would be accelerating and then decelerating hard between the two apexes. This would probably feel fast, as they would be driving the whole time just as they are used to in standard corners. Unfortunately, this would be slower than optimal because they didn't take the most efficient path. They didn't follow the **Double Apex Rule**.

THE **DOUBLE APEX RULE**

As you drive between the two apexes at the limit, you should aim to not need a speed reversal. By that, we mean you should not accelerate and then decelerate between the two apexes or vice versa. After you pass the 1st apex, reaching the 2nd apex in the most efficient manner will either require a reduction in speed (and radius), an increase in speed (and radius,) or close to a constant speed (and radius). The goal is to drive at the limit between the apexes while steadily changing your speed (and radius.) By doing this, you drive the most efficient path possible and link the two apexes. If you need a later, slower corner exit, you drive the 1st apex faster and earlier. If you need an earlier, faster corner exit, you drive the 1st apex slower and later. This is exactly as if optimizing a standard corner except the 2nd apex reverses what you do at the 1st apex.

If you pass the 1st apex and have a steady change in speed that allows you to just barely touch the 2nd apex at which point your acceleration arc gives an optimal corner exit, you know you did the double apex properly.

This means however, that you can not only make a mistake in how you drive the entry and exit to link the two apexes, but also in how efficiently you move between them. For example, if you start decelerating more than necessary after the 1st apex and then realize you need to then accelerate at some point to meet the 2nd apex, you haven't linked your apex angles. If you need a speed reversal to reach the 2nd apex then your path between the two is taking unnecessarily longer than it could and/or that you've compromised your entry and/or exit.

Needing to do a speed reversal to reach the 2nd apex can also guide you in how to drive the double apex however. For example, if you go past the 1st apex too fast and early, you could take the most efficient path to the 2nd apex with a steady change in speed and radius. This would cause too late and slow of an exit as we saw earlier with the linked apex angles.

Alternatively, if you quickly noticed that you passed the 1st apex too fast and early, you could continue decelerating hard past the 1st apex and then start accelerating well before the 2nd apex to give you the best corner exit currently achievable considering the 1st apex mistake. This will cause your path between the two apexes to be longer than necessary, but it will let you know that you need to do the 1st apex a little later and slower.

If you pass the 1st apex and then have a steady change in speed that allows you to just barely touch the 2nd apex at which point your acceleration arc gives you an optimal corner exit, you know you did the double apex properly. It may sound hard to keep track of your speed through the corner and make sure you don't reverse it, but we aren't saying you should be watching your speedometer through a corner. We can use some basic car control cues to help us in this process.

The Andretti Hairpin at Laguna Seca. A double apex?

DOUBLE APEX CUES

Driving between the two apexes is different from a standard corner in that we don't have an ideal direction anymore. Because of this, driving a double apex properly can feel like you are making a mistake. Once you get used to decelerating and accelerating as quickly as possible in standard corners, going for a steady change in speed and radius, even if driven at the limit, can feel slow.

To achieve this steady change in speed, a good cue to pay attention to is the steering wheel movement. When driving at the limit, a change in speed equals a change in radius and therefore steering position. Since the radius at each apex will require a certain steering wheel position, your goal should be to have your **average** steering wheel position steadily change from the 1st apex to the 2nd apex. It's important to understand this is the average position however. You absolutely should be doing your steering wheel movement testing to make sure you stay at the limit. Trying to stay at the limit as best you can between the two apexes is very important to maintain the efficiency desired.

> Your goal should be to have your average steering wheel position steadily change from the 1st apex to the 2nd apex.

It's also key to only focus on the steering wheel movement as a cue, not the pedal movement. Sometimes the throttle and brake inputs needed could be misleading. Many racetracks feature long decreasing radius double apexes that need you to start while close to or at full throttle and then switch to braking and turning as you slow down. This may feel like you are doing a reversal of speed even though you are constantly decelerating. If the average steering wheel movement to maintain the limit is steadily changing however, you'll know the car is steadily decreasing its radius and speed as well.

This also shows how important a driver's car control skills are in being able to determine a proper line. Using the steering wheel to determine that you are following the Double Apex Rule only works if you are using it properly. A driver should not just force the steering to move from one position to another going into greater amounts of understeer. Driven at the limit, the speed the car is traveling will determine the correct steering wheel position and it's a driver's job to find it and keep it there. A driver should use the brakes to reduce the car's speed, not tire scrub from extreme understeer.

Another good cue you can use for a double apex is engine speed. This auditory cue allows you to have a pretty good idea if you have a steady rate of speed change without having to look at the speedometer. If you have to shift during the double apex, this can cause problems, so it should probably be considered more secondary to the steering wheel, but listening to engine speed can be helpful as well.

Finally, although we aren't concerned with using the Universal Cue to maximize our acceleration in one ideal direction, the overall movement of the car in relation to the corner is still of the utmost importance. Just as in standard corners, the Universal Cue will be the final answer that provides ultimate precision. Sensitivity to the Universal Cue will allow you to visualize the path the vehicle is traveling on in relation to the corner as a whole and this is the primary way you will not only be able to optimize a double apex, but also correct mistakes as early as possible.

The vehicle's speed, radius, and steering wheel position should steadily change from the 1st apex to the 2nd.

THE CLASSIC **DOUBLE APEX** – ANDRETTI HAIRPIN

Okay, enough with the cones and theory. Let's go through some real world examples now to see how the Double Apex Rule works on track. Well actually, if you notice the cone placement in this illustration, the corner we've been working up this whole time was the Andretti Hairpin at Laguna Seca. This corner is ideally driven as double apex in just about any car and the two apexes are very close to the same radius requiring a very circular path between them.

The technique of how to optimize a double apex is not commonly known however, so many drivers get confused as to how to drive the Andretti Hairpin and you will see all sorts of different approaches. Many times, drivers will attempt to continue braking past the 1st apex and treat it as one corner. The geometry of the hairpin doesn't make that a viable approach however. You wouldn't be able to spiral all the way to the 2nd apex and would need to start accelerating before you reached it. Unfortunately however, some drivers have been taught this is actually a good thing.

THE **DOUBLE APEX** MYTH

This illustration shows how some drivers have been taught is the proper way to tackle a double apex. That they should decelerate deep into the corner past the 1st apex and then accelerate out past the 2nd apex. Does this misconception look familiar to one we've looked at this in past?

You might recognize this as a similar error to the myth of the super late apex from *The Perfect Corner*. While your apex speed at cone 3 as well as corner exit speed would be higher, the problem is the extra **time** spent between cone 2 and 3 because this is a less efficient, longer path than would be ideal.

Just as in the super late apex, at the same point in **time** that this driver makes it to cone 3 (even if their apex speed is higher at that point) the optimized line driver would already be further down the track at a higher speed.

Myths like this carry on because the difference in time between the optimal and this approach is very small. We're talking small fractions of a second difference. This illustration shows how we've added a cone that only slightly changes the corner geometry, but would be in the way of our previous optimal line. Guess what? This corner is now optimized and the double apex myth line is now ideal. Just that little difference will change how you optimize this corner. A key takeaway here is that although in our illustrations the color-coded lines may look quite different, the speed of the car at any given point would be very similar. A more skilled driver could beat drivers of lesser car control abilities using either method.

Unless that skillful driver knew the ideal method however, they might never even try doing the corner a different way if they are already beating everybody.

Examples like this hopefully help you to understand the importance of knowing the ideal technique even if the difference is minor. It takes away confusion and gives you a solid goal to focus on as you search for those last 10ths. Understand that car control is still a huge part of the equation however. Don't expect to start blowing away the competition immediately. There will still be a lot of training needed to give yourself that advantage over other drivers.

OPTIMAL **ENTRY** AND **EXIT**

While we are on the subject of how not to do a double apex, we also wanted to cover what is essentially the opposite version of the double apex myth. While the double apex myth has you decelerate and then accelerate between the two apexes, what would happen if you tried it the other way around as shown in this illustration and accelerated first?

Remember, a driver should travel the shortest, fastest route between the two apexes **that allows an optimal entry and exit**.

This last part is quite important because if all you are concerned with is the shortest, fastest route, you would drive the corner as depicted here. This shows what would happen if a driver tried to apply standard Line Theory rules to a double apex. They would successfully reduce the time between the apexes, but this would only be possible by severely compromising the entry and exit.

The more circular shaped path we use with the Double Apex Rule is not the absolute shortest, fastest route possible. It is merely the shortest, fastest route that allows you to still optimize the entry and exit. You have to do it all to drive the double apex correctly. The previous illustration simply shows the absolute fastest way to go between the two apexes ignoring the entry and exit. The driver would use maximum throttle with an acceleration arc after the 1st apex that leads directly into a trail braking entry spiral toward the 2nd apex. The ideal directions between the two apexes would be pointing toward each other and this would be optimal if they were simply trying to get from the 1st to the 2nd apex as quickly as possible.

You could see however, that this doesn't allow an optimal entry and exit before and after the double apex portion because the apex speeds are too slow. If we increased the apex speeds to optimize the entry and exit, the paths between the apexes would never be able to meet up in the middle.

These apexes are just too close together to allow an optimal acceleration arc and then deceleration spiral between them. This is the very essence of why you use the Double Apex Rule when maximum acceleration and deceleration is just not possible without compromising yourself elsewhere. Only when the two apexes are far enough apart that you can optimize both their entries and exits independently do you no longer need the Double Apex Rule because then you have two completely separate corners.

OVER **90-DEGREE ENTRY** – OAK TREE (VIR)

So here we are back at Oak Tree again and we can now show you the correct solution. You can see here how Oak Tree is a double apex because the total entry angle to the 2nd apex requires a good bit more than the 90-degree limit allows. It is also different from the Andretti Hairpin in that you will be significantly decreasing your radius between the two apexes. Prior to the 1st apex you are reducing your radius as quickly as possible as in a standard corner. But then, between the two apexes your radius will steadily decrease to what allows you to just barely meet the 2nd apex.

You'll see this sort of double apex somewhat often and it is quite confusing for many drivers. While you are still turning and braking all the way to the 2nd apex, your goal switches as you pass the 1st apex from all-out radius reduction to a steady radius reduction linking your two apexes. This can feel slow and as if you are losing time, even though you are doing the optimal. In some cars, just the tire drag and aero friction might be sufficient to decrease the speed and radius to the correct amount, but in others, some braking might still be required as well.

LONG **DOUBLE APEX** – BIG BEND (LIME ROCK)

Another time you might need to use the Double Apex Rule is with long "carousel" type turns such as Big Bend at Lime Rock. The common thread is that again, you will be unable find a single apex that allows you to achieve maximum deceleration and acceleration before and after it. Because Big Bend is so high speed, many cars will need to apply a good bit of throttle to overcome aero drag even though there is actually a radius and speed reduction needed between the two apexes.

Not all long corners need to be double apexed however. As a general rule, the longer, narrower, and more squared off a corner is, the less likely you will be able to find a single apex and will need to apply the Double Apex Rule.

The entry and exit conditions can also affect things as well. If this same corner had a low entry speed, it would most likely become a single apex corner where you carry throttle deep into your entry spiral. It always depends on how each car's capabilities fit in with each corner so only individual testing will give you the answer.

OVER **90-DEGREE EXIT** – ROAD ATLANTA SHORT

Sometimes long corners can be quite tricky however. The short-configuration connecting corner at Road Atlanta will fool many drivers.

Limit cornering ends

90 Degree Limit

It has a squared off entry that forces a 1st apex at that point and then a long exit with a radius that will often closely match the acceleration arc of many lower-powered cars. A more circular exit line is very realistic in this corner because it's fast and goes uphill. Many low-powered cars aren't able to accelerate much during the exit, if at all.

This corner causes confusion because you might think this illustration shows the ideal solution treating the corner as a single apex. Following Line Theory, you would find an earlier apex angle that would allow you to barely stay on track with a full-throttle corner exit. This would probably feel ideal, but there is a problem.

You would still be cornering well past 90 degrees into your exit. As we learned earlier, this causes you to effectively cancel out some of the tire forces generated earlier in the corner exit. The result of this is an unnecessarily long line on the outside of the track that will take more time to complete than a more efficient shorter line. Notice how far out on the track the line took the car.

90 Degree Limit

This illustration however, shows the correct solution. You would start at the same basic 1st apex, but pass it later and slower. You would then follow the Double Apex Rule and drive at the limit along the inside of the track until you reach a point where you can begin your acceleration arc. This is where your 2nd apex is.

The interesting part here is that because of the speed and shape of the corner, a lower-powered car will already be at full throttle during the double apex portion. They won't have the power for their acceleration arc to push them away from the inside of the track if they don't start it from the 1st apex and break the 90-degree limit. So even though the car would be at full throttle the whole time right next to the inside of the track, the point that the car is no longer able to maintain the limit is technically the 2nd apex. They would then be in a full-throttle corner by the inside of the track the rest of the way. A full-throttle corner is essentially a straight and we'll look in depth at how to optimize those later in the book.

A more powerful car would do it the same way except they wouldn't be at full throttle through the double apex portion and would then have the power for their acceleration arc to carry them away from the inside of the track at the 2nd apex. This acceleration arc might not push them to the very outside edge of the track, but if they are pushed from the inside edge of the track at all, their second apex must start at a point no earlier than 90-degrees before the following straight.

The key here is that anytime you start an acceleration arc that forces you away from the inside of the track, cornering should be complete by 90 degrees from that point. You might not be on a typical "straight" yet, but you should either be traveling straight or if the corner is not over yet, you should be at full throttle by the inside of the track.

Dealing with combining double apexes, 90-degree limits and full-throttle corners can be quite confusing so we'll look at some other similar sequences later. We'll also examine some ways of figuring out where exactly the 90-degree limit might be and how to identify it as you drive.

DOUBLE APEXING A HAIRPIN

Sometimes you might even need to use the Double Apex Rule in situations that look nothing at all like a typical double apex. When looking at the Suzuka hairpin back in *The Perfect Corner,* we rather glazed over the specifics of how you might need to optimize it in a high-acceleration car.

You can see in this illustration how even if you use all 90 degrees of the entry spiral, you will come close, but not quite be able to make it to the inside of the track at the apex. If you tried to accelerate at the point this entry spiral actually hits the inside of the track, you would run wide at exit. If you tried to use a later, slower spiral to hit the inside of the track, your apex speed would be too slow for an ideal exit. You won't find a singular apex here that will allow you to optimize both your entry and exit in a high-acceleration car. Sound familiar? That's right – we will need to use the Double Apex Rule.

Not all hairpins will require this, as it depends on the specific shape. If for instance, the inside of the track was pointier, you could slide the whole line over to the left to optimize for that one point. If you tried to do that here however, you would need to drive on the grass because the inside is rounded. Lower-powered cars with a more circular exit normally don't have this problem either because of their earlier apex. Their optimal line is more open and rounded which makes it less likely to hit the inside of the track more than once. You also won't have this problem when apexing a cone because your entry spiral and acceleration arc are not being blocked by a portion of the inside of the track. They only touch the cone once during the transition at the apex.

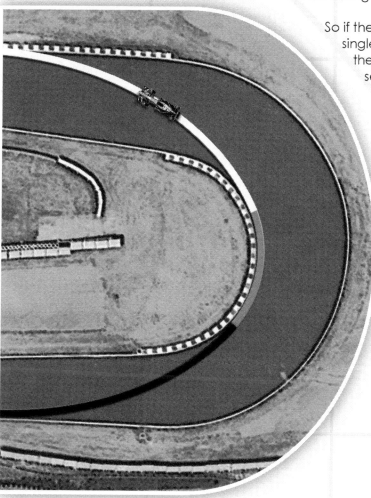

So if the track shape doesn't allow a single apex, the solution is to use the Double Apex Rule. You can see in this illustration how the driver will do their standard entry spiral until they meet the inside of the track and then hug the inside curb until the earliest point they are able to begin their acceleration arc.

You would use the same apex finding techniques as described earlier, but since the inside curb is basically a constant radius here, you just follow it around.

It's always a good idea to try to find a single apex first as that is ultimately faster, but many 180-degree corners are squared off on the inside like the Andretti hairpin or rounded like Suzuka. You won't be able to find a single apex on either, so it's not a mistake if you need to follow the Double Apex Rule and drive a constant speed for a bit as you move as efficiently as possible to the point you can start accelerating.

Also, in case you were thinking that it's probably not worth worrying about such a minor detail and the car had already gotten really close to the apex in the first illustration, we've overlaid them here.

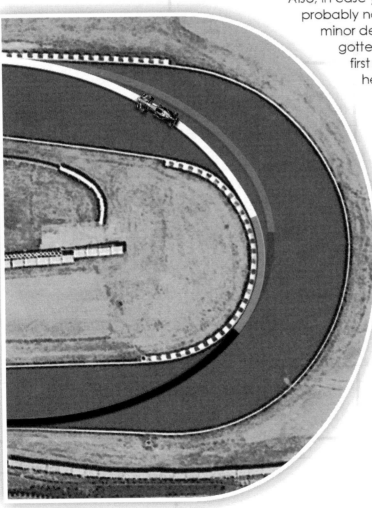

Although it may look like the car got very close to the apex before, you can see here how just that small difference can significantly change the total line. Not only was the original line longer, but it also had a lower minimum speed.

It may seem like this is a fairly rare situation that is only limited to hairpin turns, but this same principle can actually be applied to virtually every corner you drive.

CORRECTING WITH THE **DOUBLE APEX RULE**

It's important to understand that while we call this principle the Double Apex Rule, its real purpose is to find the most efficient path when we can't use the width of the track to increase entry and exit speed. This does not only apply to double apexes.

This can be a situation you run into in any corner if you've over-slowed your entry. From a Line Theory standpoint, once you've entered a corner, there is only two states that you can be in that you will constantly try to correct. You can be too fast to make the apex or you can be too slow. You will never truly be on a perfect line. If you are going too fast, the rules don't change. You will continue to reduce your radius as quickly as possible to the point that you are able to begin your currently ideal acceleration arc. Depending on the corner shape, this will sometimes just adjust your apex along the inside of the track or it might move it away from inside as well.

When you're slower than optimal as you approach the apex however, and continued radius reduction would carry you off the inside of the track, the rules will change. You certainly can't continue with maximum radius reduction and you also wouldn't be at the point yet that you could begin your acceleration arc. This problem should hopefully sound familiar now because yet again, we need to use the Double Apex Rule.

Once you enter your spiral, your goal is to get to the angle you can begin your acceleration arc as quickly as possible. As we've learned, ideally this will require you to reduce your radius as quickly as possible to just barely pass the ideal apex. But if through an error in car control, line prediction, or simply playing it safe, you find you're going too slow, a change in approach will be needed

If you are going just a little too slow, you might simply need to marginally lessen your braking and not reduce your radius as quickly as you were previously. Still driving at the limit, but now having a slightly more circular path. If you over-slowed even more, you might need to maintain your current speed to the apex with neutral throttle on a circular path. If you've made a large error and seriously over-slowed the entry, you might even need to accelerate some to the apex, increasing your radius. The key is that as soon as you realize you over-slowed, you want to ensure that you follow the Double Apex Rule. The place you realize your error becomes the 1st apex and the new ideal corner apex becomes your 2nd apex. You want to drive at the limit from one to the other as quickly as possible without needing a speed reversal.

> Once you enter your spiral, your goal is to reach the angle you can begin your acceleration arc as quickly as possible.

As with all error corrections however, this is a constant process and what we are describing here is what corner entry mastery is all about. Your normal corner entry goals and using the Double Apex Rule are not an either/or proposition. You will constantly be balancing the two because your goal is simply to get to the angle that allows an ideal acceleration arc as quickly as possible. As with all Line Theory rules, it's useful to memorize them, but even more important to understand the principles at work. That way you will be able to drive intuitively by directly following the physics that will lower your lap times.

While we've learned you might use the Double Apex Rule anywhere, traditional double apex corners are fairly rare. Many tracks don't even have a single one. There is however, a much more common compromise corner that almost every road course in the world features.

ANOTHER COMPROMISE (**THE CHICANE**)

Known also as esses and having many different variations, we will simply call this other compromise by its most common name, the chicane. This is also the final type of corner you will need to learn. Every corner on a racetrack is either a standard corner, double apex, or chicane. That's it. These different types of corners will be placed together in various combinations, but everything can be broken down into these three types.

> Every corner on a racetrack is either a standard corner, double apex, or chicane.

At the end of the book we'll take a look at complex corner sequences, how they fit together and break them down piece by piece, but first let's take a closer look at the chicane and see how to apply Line Theory principles to optimize one. While a chicane can take many different shapes, they will always have the key similarity of requiring a direction change while driving at the limit. For while a double apex is essentially two turns that are close together going in the same direction, a chicane is two turns in opposite directions.

Not coincidentally, the solution is yet again to find the shortest, most efficient path between the two apexes that can be driven at the limit, but that also still allows an optimal entry and exit. The way we accomplish this however, should be much more familiar than the Double Apex Rule. To start off, let's take a look at a classic, textbook chicane so we can learn this new skill one step at a time.

THE CLASSIC **CHICANE** – ROAD ATLANTA 10A-B

Historically, racetracks didn't feature many chicanes, but as speeds grew and safety become a greater concern, track designs started to incorporate them to slow the cars down. The chicane at Road Atlanta is a perfect example because it was put in later as a safety measure and is the classic chicane layout requiring drivers to make a transition from one direction to the other mid track.

Like the double apex, how to optimize a chicane is often misunderstood by many drivers and several different approaches are often advocated. Yet again however, there is only one optimal solution.

In principle, the technique for optimizing a chicane is the same as for a double apex. You will drive between the two apexes on the shortest, most efficient path possible that still allows an optimal entry and exit. But while efficiency is yet again the goal, we can actually use our standard Line Theory rules to achieve it. The key difference is that in a chicane, you will set your own ideal directions just as we did with the cones earlier. Unfortunately however, we also have to deal with an unavoidable law of physics as well. The driver's arch-nemesis, yaw inertia.

THE IDEAL **CHICANE** VS **YAW INERTIA**

In some respects, optimizing a chicane is fairly straightforward, so to start off let's enlist the aid of our astronaut again as we explore this. This time, our astronaut has been given some anti-gravity boots that allow him to fly through the chicane as shown below. There is nothing in this illustration we haven't seen before, we are simply combining several spirals where one leads to the next.

The dashed line shows the astronauts path. He starts from the bottom left and does his entry spiral to the 1st apex followed by an acceleration arc to his current position in the illustration. He will then do another entry spiral to the 2nd apex and a final acceleration arc to the following straight. The arrows show his ideal directions during each portion and the circles show his attainable speed at each apex.

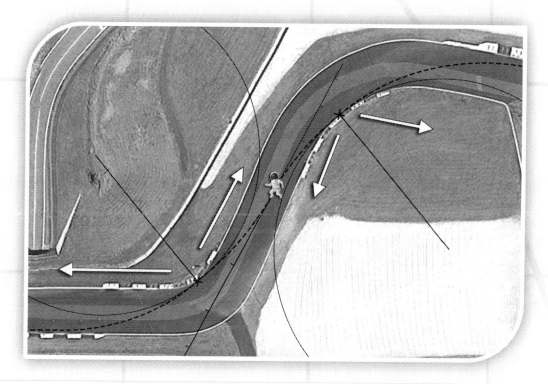

This illustration now shows why chicane optimization is able to use standard Line Theory rules. We've added some cones in the middle of the track to show that we are essentially optimizing two separate corners. The straights before and after have normal track edges so their ideal directions are set, but in the middle of the chicane we get to decide. We can choose our own ideal direction as we pass the cones just as we did earlier. Notice however, that the ideal directions we have chosen are exactly opposite each other. This is because the end of the 1st corner is simply the beginning of the 2nd. The ideal directions must match as you transition. Where exactly this transition needs to take place will depend on the 1st and 2nd corners geometry as well as the vehicle's acceleration arc.

Everything is looking pretty straightforward so far, so why are we using the astronaut for this example and what does all this have anything to do with yaw inertia?

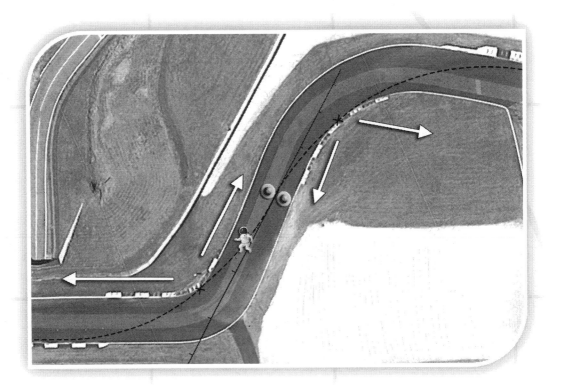

To introduce the yaw inertia problem we are facing here, let's put a lower-powered car through the chicane that has a circular acceleration arc. You can see in this illustration how everything looks fairly similar to before with a few small differences. First off, both apexes are earlier and faster as you would expect for a lower-powered car. These earlier apexes cause the other noticeable difference as well, which is that the transition is much closer to the 2nd apex. Remember, where the transition ideally takes place is dictated by the corner geometry as well as the acceleration arc of the vehicle. In this case, the more circular acceleration arc caused the change.

While the transition may have shifted somewhat from the one our astronaut did, everything still looks pretty good. So where is the problem?

This Illustration now shows what is happening during the transition and where the inherent problem with the chicane lies. As the vehicle transitions in the middle of the chicane, the steering should theoretically move instantaneously from the turned position required at the end of the first acceleration arc to directly straight as is needed at the beginning of the spiral to the 2nd apex. Clearly, this theoretical ideal isn't possible.

We didn't have this problem with our astronaut, as he doesn't have a steering wheel. He doesn't need to rotate and so would have no yaw inertia. Even if he flew on a circular path such as this, he would be able to immediately start blasting his extinguisher in the opposite direction during the transition. This also wouldn't be much of a problem in a high-power car that had an acceleration arc that matched the astronaut's. The driver would steadily unwind the steering during the exit so it would reach center as the car transitioned to the entry spiral. Remember though, almost no car will have a perfect spiral acceleration arc; most will be at least somewhat more circular.

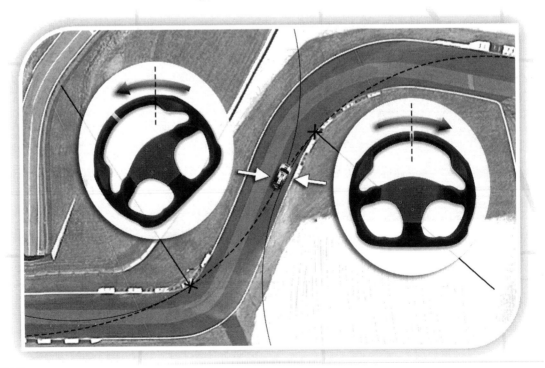

So with our low-acceleration car, we have to deal with this transition in a less ideal way. We have to compromise by taking some time to unwind the steering wheel as we transition. You might be thinking "big deal," how long would it really take to unwind the steering wheel? The problem isn't the steering wheel movement however; it's what that steering movement does to the car. The faster we unwind, the faster the car will rotate and because of yaw inertia, the car will tend to oversteer when we try to reverse that rotation rate.

For many cars, the center of a chicane can create yaw accelerations that essentially mimic the Scandinavian flick and will give the vehicle a tendency to oversteer as the vehicle transitions. The faster the transition and the more circular the initial acceleration arc, the greater the tendency. If you've ever seen a car do a little wiggle at track out when a driver suddenly straightens the steering wheel, it's because of the yaw inertia. A circular acceleration arc wants this late unwinding, but if done too fast, the problems created by yaw inertia outweigh the benefits of the ideal acceleration arc.

Therefore, during a chicane, this creates a dilemma with no clear-cut answer. The driver wants to transition as quickly as possible, but also must deal with the yaw inertia. A stiffly sprung car with a centralized mass such as a formula car minimizes this yaw inertia problem, but at least some compromise will almost always be required. Well known Formula 1 coach Rob Wilson advocates having a "flat spot" in the middle of a chicane and we believe he is recommending a driver remove all yaw velocity during the transition by holding the steering at center momentarily. While this might be a good approach for a very stiff, high-acceleration Formula one car, it is most likely more efficient for most cars not to completely stop rotating, even for a split second. Most cars wouldn't have the power to keep the tires at the limit and would lose efficiency during this split-second "flat spot" driving straight. In general, as a car transitions in the chicane, it is most likely faster for a driver to unwind fast enough to carry at least some yaw velocity through into the entry spiral. This will have the effect of making their entry spiral a little more circular as if they entered it a bit later.

OPTIMIZING A **CHICANE**

Just as with the transition to acceleration in a standard corner, how much to compromise a chicane from the ideal will depend on the driver's abilities as well as the car's capabilities. It might seem like we are making a big deal of this compromise, but a driver with solid car control skills will generally be able to learn quite quickly how fast they can transition in each car.

Now that we understand the inherent yaw inertia compromise a driver will have to face, we can move on to actually optimizing the chicane. As we like to do things from the driver's perspective, we'll approach this in the way you might work up a new chicane.

The first step to optimizing a chicane is to drive the 1st apex as if you are driving any standard corner. This time however, you will aim to generally have your acceleration arc take you somewhere in the middle of the track. Again, we won't know how we did until the corner is over. It's just a prediction at this point. As you accelerate, you will be eyeing the second corner because when you predict switching to an entry spiral will have the car just barely pass the 2nd apex, you initiate your transition. If you are able to just reach the 2nd apex and then your acceleration arc gives you an ideal corner exit, you'll know you've optimized the chicane. Doing the chicane in this manner gives us the shortest, straightest, and fastest path between the two apexes that allows an optimal entry and exit.

As in any corner however, we will never be perfect so based on the mistakes we make, we can refine our approach to the chicane. Did we hit the apex, but it was too early? Too late? Did we miss the apex? We'll start troubleshooting in a minute but first let's see if we can create a new rule to help us in the process. Beyond following the basic rules of Line Theory, the only new rule that a driver will need to worry about is centered around the transition.

THE **CHICANE RULE**

We've already talked about the unique nature of the transition phase and the compromise it creates, but it will also allow us to ensure we are optimizing a chicane. The Chicane Rule is based around this transition. **To optimize a chicane, a driver should maximize acceleration from the 1st apex through to the <u>end</u> of the transition at which point an entry spiral to the 2nd apex should create an optimum corner exit.**

A driver's goal is to need immediate deceleration after the transition. If they have to decelerate before the end of the transition or they don't have to decelerate until closer to the 2nd apex, they'll know they made a mistake and need to adjust their first apex.

The greater the deceleration needed after the transition, the greater the speed that was achieved during the chicane. The higher the average speed through the chicane without compromising the entry or exit, the straighter the line that is required. The straighter the line, the shorter, faster, and more efficient it is. Neat how that works, isn't it?

Following this rule will allow you to detect any mistakes in how you drive a chicane. If you need to slow down to make the 2nd apex **before** completing the transition, you'll know you need a later, slower 1st apex. If you don't **have** to decelerate right after the transition to make the 2nd apex then you need an earlier, faster 1st apex.

We also want to emphasize that the deceleration phase after the transition will have no straight-line braking. A driver should immediately enter their spiral. Also just as in standard corners, the entry spiral might not include actual trail braking. For example, in chicane layouts such as the one at Road Atlanta, a low-acceleration car will be very close to the 2nd apex by the time the transition phase is over. The entry spiral to the 2nd apex will often be short enough where only a full or partial throttle lift will be practical.

Lastly, always remember the basic Line Theory rule that you must not decelerate past an apex. This may seem obvious, but it becomes important to remember in really short chicanes that we'll look at later.

The esses at Road Atlanta is optimized as a series of chicanes in high-acceleration cars, but as full-throttle corners for lower-powered ones.

CHICANE CUES

To help you along in this process, let's now look at the cues a driver can pay attention to as they tackle a chicane to ensure that they are working toward the ideal solution. Most of the cues used while driving a chicane will be the same ones used while driving a standard corner. The entrance and exit should be done in the same way where you should ideally use the Universal Cue to optimize the entry spiral and acceleration arc. As usual, the ideal directions will follow the angle of the track edge. During the chicane, you do the same optimization except you will need to choose your own ideal direction as if you had placed a cone out in the middle of the track. This cone will set your ideal direction in the same way it did earlier in the book. Your transition will be centered on this imaginary cone.

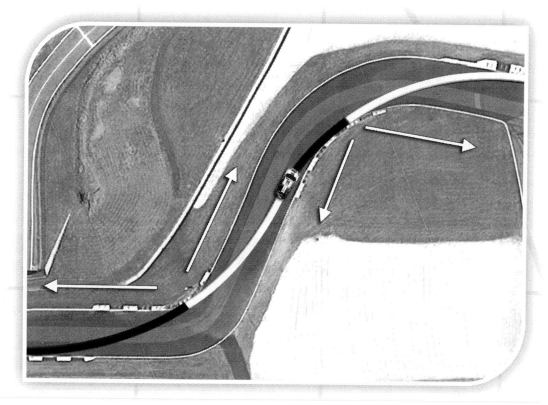

While it will be up to each driver how quickly they feel they can transition, remember that you should be maximizing acceleration all the way through to the end of the transition phase at which point you should immediately need to decelerate. Therefore it's quite important to know exactly when the transition phase is over. A useful shortcut here is that the steering wheel will be straight again. As soon as your transition has reached the point that your steering wheel goes past center toward the 2nd apex, you should begin your deceleration spiral. How quickly you move the steering across the center will determine how much yaw velocity you create. A quick movement from maximum steering in one direction to the other will create a lot of yaw velocity. A steering movement that has a momentary pause in the center, a "flat spot," will minimize it.

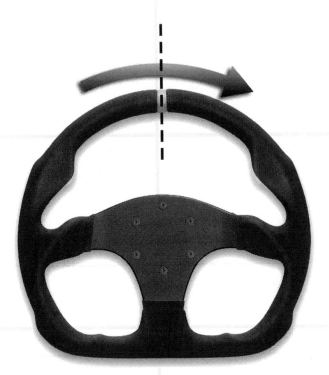

If you were too early and fast through the 1st apex, you would need to decelerate before the steering went back past center if you wished to make the 2nd apex. If your 1st apex were too late and slow, you would be able to continue accelerating after the transition was over and wouldn't need to decelerate until you were closer to the 2nd apex. You might even be able to accelerate through both apexes without having to lift. Unfortunately, some drivers have been taught that this is the proper way to do a chicane and this takes us to yet another myth.

The transition phase of a chicane is over when the steering wheel has gone back past center in the direction of the 2nd apex.

THE **CHICANE** MYTH

Thankfully, this is the last of our myths, and the faulty reasoning should look quite familiar as it again deals with early acceleration based on distance, not time. There is sometimes the misconception that you should slow down enough for the 1st apex to try to allow full throttle through the entire chicane. This would require a very late and slow 1st apex that might even allow the car to touch the inside edge of the track. If you follow the Chicane Rule, you won't be able to touch the close edge of the track in a chicane unless you've already touched the far edge. If that happens however, you aren't in a chicane anymore; you officially have two separate corners.

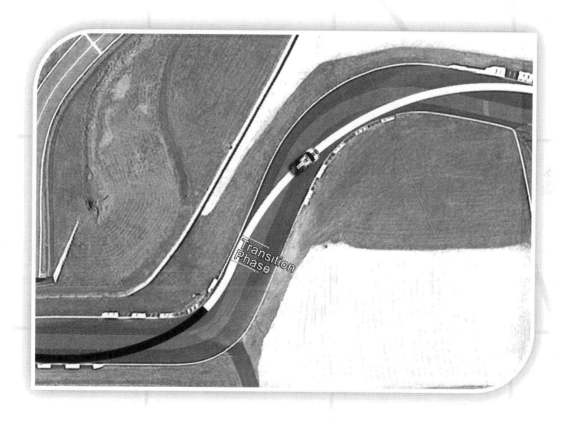

Like the other myths, the problem is that even though the corner exit speed can be higher, the amount of time to reach that speed is also higher. As suggested by the myth, the transition phase leads directly into further acceleration and it's very early in the chicane. This is never the correct way to do a chicane, as you would severely compromise your entry speed and therefore total time. You should need to decelerate right after the transition. Full throttle through a chicane should only be possible if no braking was required before the 1st apex or if you reach the far edge and don't have to lift to make the 2nd apex. But of course, if either of these happen, then you no longer have a chicane, you have a full-throttle corner.

As mentioned earlier, sometimes you might do a chicane with only the very smallest of throttle lifts, but that would only be if your transition phase is extremely late in the chicane and very nearly reaches the 2nd apex. This only happens however, because the driver is carrying so much speed through the 1st apex. Sometimes your transition will be right after the 1st apex, but only because there is a lot of deceleration needed to reach the 2nd apex. You would never transition right after the 1st apex and then continue accelerating through the 2nd apex.

Using the Chicane Rule will give a driver a concrete goal and will allow them to avoid and spot these mistakes if they happen, but just like a double apex, working up a chicane can be quite difficult, especially longer ones. Since the apex speeds and angles are connected, you are essentially trying to optimize the corner exit of the 2nd apex on your approach to the 1st. Many times, you won't even be able to see the final corner exit until you are deep in the chicane. This will naturally lead to a good bit of repetition and fine-tuning needed before you finally come to a good solution. There is a technique you can use to help speed up the process however.

IMAGINARY CONES

Let's now go to the final turn sequence before the front straight at Barber Motorsports Park. This track features many complex corner combinations, but the final one is best described as a long chicane. The two corners are not spread out enough to separate them completely, but they are far enough apart that the resulting chicane line is very S shaped, especially for lower-powered cars. This S shape will make it easier to visualize changes as we troubleshoot this sequence.

It's important to understand that the track edges in the middle of a chicane are meaningless - they are red herrings. Only the apexes need to be optimized. Therefore, a useful way to work up a chicane is to give yourself an imaginary cone in the middle that signifies the track edge that you will optimize for. You can often find a reference point right on the track for this such as a crack or tire mark, but you should use your overall spatial awareness as well. You will optimize for this point as if it's a corner exit cone for the 1st apex. This will set your mid-

Transition Phase

chicane ideal directions as well as your transition point. Your ideal directions will point directly toward each other and will be at the same angle as the car as it passes the imaginary cone. The transition would theoretically be instantaneous right at the cone, but as we've learned, this typically won't be possible so we've given the driver a transition phase to allow time to accomplish this. We can then take what happens after the transition to move around our imaginary cone until we've optimized the entire sequence.

If the imaginary cone were too far out toward the edge of the track as in this illustration, the driver would carry too much speed as they transitioned toward the 2nd apex and this would cause too early and fast of a final corner exit and send them off track if they didn't correct. If they spot their error early enough, the driver could minimize acceleration or even decelerate before the transition was complete. This will allow them to stay on track and save the corner exit although there would of course be a lap time penalty from the optimum.

Imaginary Cone Too Far Out
= Exit Too Early and Fast

Needed
Braking Point

Transition Phase

Remember, a driver should maximize acceleration until the transition is over and the steering has gone back past center. If they need to lift at some point before this to make the 2nd apex, they will need to move their imaginary cone further in.

If the imaginary cone were too close to the near side of the track however, the driver would be too slow as they reach the transition phase. If they then decelerated to the 2nd apex as usual, they would severely compromise their final corner exit speed. Once the driver realized they are too late and slow through the 1st apex, they could correct by continuing to accelerate to the 2nd apex as long as possible before needing to brake. If their 1st apex was only a little too late and slow, their needed braking point would simply be closer to the 2nd apex as shown below. If they were excessively late and slow through the 1st apex however, they might be able to accelerate through the entire remainder of the sequence. These errors would tell the driver they need to move their imaginary cone further out toward the far side of the track.

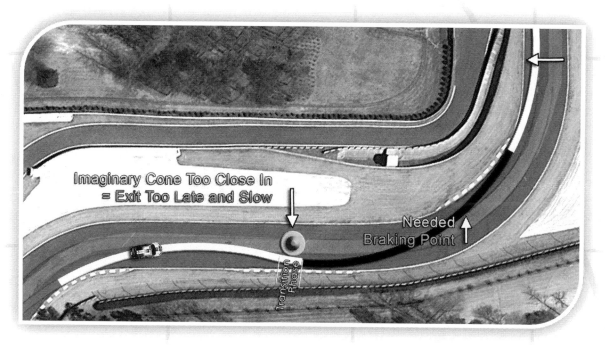

Using this imaginary cone, a driver will be able to essentially split the chicane into two separate corners that can each be optimized through standard Line Theory rules. The Chicane Rule however, is used to tell you where this imaginary cone and thus the transition between these two standard corners needs to be.

Again, the Chicane Rule is to use maximum acceleration from the 1st apex through the transition and as soon as the transition is over, immediate deceleration to the 2nd apex should be required. If this provides an ideal final corner exit, you'll know you've optimized the chicane and your imaginary cone is set correctly.

In chicanes with fairly equal radius corners, this will generally cause the imaginary cone and resultant line to be centered toward the middle of the track. A chicane with a more open second corner will need an imaginary cone further toward the far edge. A chicane with a tighter second corner will naturally need an imaginary cone closer to the near edge. The car's acceleration capability will have a similar effect as well where the higher-acceleration cars will need a cone closer to the near side and lower-acceleration ones will need one closer to the far side.

This process automatically balances the apexes to provide the most efficient and fastest path. If your cone and line never reach the edge of the track, you should continue to optimize with the Chicane Rule. Once you start bumping into a track edge however, the Chicane Rule will no longer be appropriate and you might have a full-throttle corner to deal with.

A CHICANE?

Turn 1 and 2 at Barcelona is a situation where what looks like a chicane might not be. Turn 2 is much more open than turn 1 so our imaginary cone would be very close to the far edge of the track. In fact, sometimes as in this example, it is the edge of the track, which is why this isn't always a chicane.

Since the driver doesn't need to immediately decelerate after the transition, this would normally tell them to move their imaginary cone further out and apex earlier and faster through turn 1. Since they are already at the edge however, the driver would know this isn't a chicane and they don't need the Chicane Rule. The driver would know turn 2 is actually a full-throttle corner, which is technically a straightaway and has its own set of rules.

We have some more chicanes to look at, but first we need to take a little detour and cover what surprisingly can sometimes be the most difficult part of a track to optimize. Plus, delving into this final technique will also help bring everything together that we've learned so far.

OPTIMIZING **STRAIGHTS**

It's somewhat ironic that the last technique we will cover is how to optimize a straight, as it's seemingly the simplest situation where you just hold full throttle and drive... straight. While this basic answer is often the case, sometimes there are track sections that blur the line between straights and corners. Even what looks like a typical straight might not be as... straightforward as one would think however. Combine this with complex corners such as chicanes and late spiral entries and you have some of the hardest to optimize sequences out there. To explore this, we'll start... straight from the beginning and build our knowledge from there.

Let's begin with the simplest possible straight connecting two corners going in the same direction. As shown in the illustration, optimizing this is as easy as having the first corner exit lead directly into the corner entry of the second and the ideal directions point directly towards each other. This is the shortest path possible between the two corners and it should hopefully be apparent that it can't be done any faster than this.

The Kink at Road America.
Straightaway or corner?

Let's now look at the same straight except the corners are going in opposite directions. Notice how we are still driving the car on the shortest path possible between the two corners. Sort of looks familiar doesn't it? Like a chicane? In a way, a straight with opposing corners is like chicane with a very long transition period. It's not a true chicane however, and we don't have to follow the Chicane Rule because you aren't balancing one apex angle with the next. Both corners are fully optimized to the very edge of the track. Notice also how we have placed a cone at the center of the straight to show how both corners are optimized around it just like a chicane transition point. You could actually put the cone anywhere along this line however as it's essentially just a really long transition period. Also realize that if you started bringing these corners together, they would eventually become an official chicane. You would need to start balancing the apexes by following the Chicane Rule and finding your optimum imaginary cone placement.

So whether it's a chicane or a straight, if you have opposing corners, you should ideally drive the shortest path possible from one corner to the next and your ideal directions should point directly toward each other. You might remember that we often say that the ideal direction is **basically** at the same angle as the track and this is the reason. Your ideal directions for each corner should point directly at the end of the previous acceleration arc and the beginning of the next entry spiral. When you have two opposing corners that are close enough together, then driving a straight line between them is normally what you want to do. Your ideal direction from one corner will directly take you to the next. You'll "chicane it," so to speak. When your straight is a bit longer however, there are some real world considerations that might have you not want to try for this ideal.

Here we have shown a more realistic scenario for an opposing corner straight of any significant length. The driver will exit and enter the turns with an ideal direction parallel to the track edge. Between the turns, this will require the driver alter their path slightly to cross the track and this will make their line a little longer than ideal. While not theoretically optimal, there are a few reasons the driver might want to do this. First off, the driver is not at the limit of traction on a straightaway. They are not having to sacrifice any power to alter their line. The only time penalty is from the extra distance traveled and for a straight of any decent length, the theoretical difference is in the 100ths of a second at most. It is essentially meaningless compared to other factors. You'll generally only start wanting to "chicane it" and have your ideal directions point toward each other and not parallel to the track edge when the straight gets short enough that the steering needed to move across is starting to cause too much induced drag.

Secondly, a driver might want to move over to start their corner entry at the edge of the track simply for practical reasons and consistency. For normal length straights, it's just not worth it to put focus on driving perfectly straight across the track to the next corner entry. The miniscule time gained is meaningless compared to the time that could be lost by not putting enough focus on the corner itself. A set braking point by the edge of the track will promote consistency and the greater starting angle will also allow more leeway for mistakes. For instance, if you drive diagonally to the next corner, you will be braking toward the edge of the track. If miss your braking point, you might go off track. With a typical parallel entry however, you would have some track space left over to correct.

THE **FULL-THROTTLE CORNER RULE***

Although we've already introduced one real world compromise you may wish to make, so far optimizing these standard straights seems pretty intuitive. Sometimes a "straight" is not actually very straight however. Something that looks like a corner can technically become a straight when no deceleration is needed. We call this a full-throttle corner as it will still have an apex like a standard corner, but the driver is at full throttle from entry to exit. This could be a high-speed corner where the car is near top speed the whole time or it could even be a lower-speed corner if the entry speed is low and the car accelerates all the way through.

The way you'll know you have a full-throttle corner to deal with is that you won't be able to drive perfectly straight from one corner to the next, but you also won't have to lift. Even though we've learned you might not always want to drive perfectly straight between corners, a full-throttle corner will make this impossible anyway because the track will be too curved to allow a straight line.

To optimize one, the **Full-Throttle Corner Rule*** is that you should **drive the shortest path possible through the full-throttle corner while reaching the limit exactly at the apex**. We'll look at the details of the rule shortly, but first we need to learn more about the nature of a full-throttle corner, as it is not as simple as it may seem at first. Also make sure you notice the asterisk on the rule. There is a pretty significant disclaimer to the rule that we'll talk about as well.

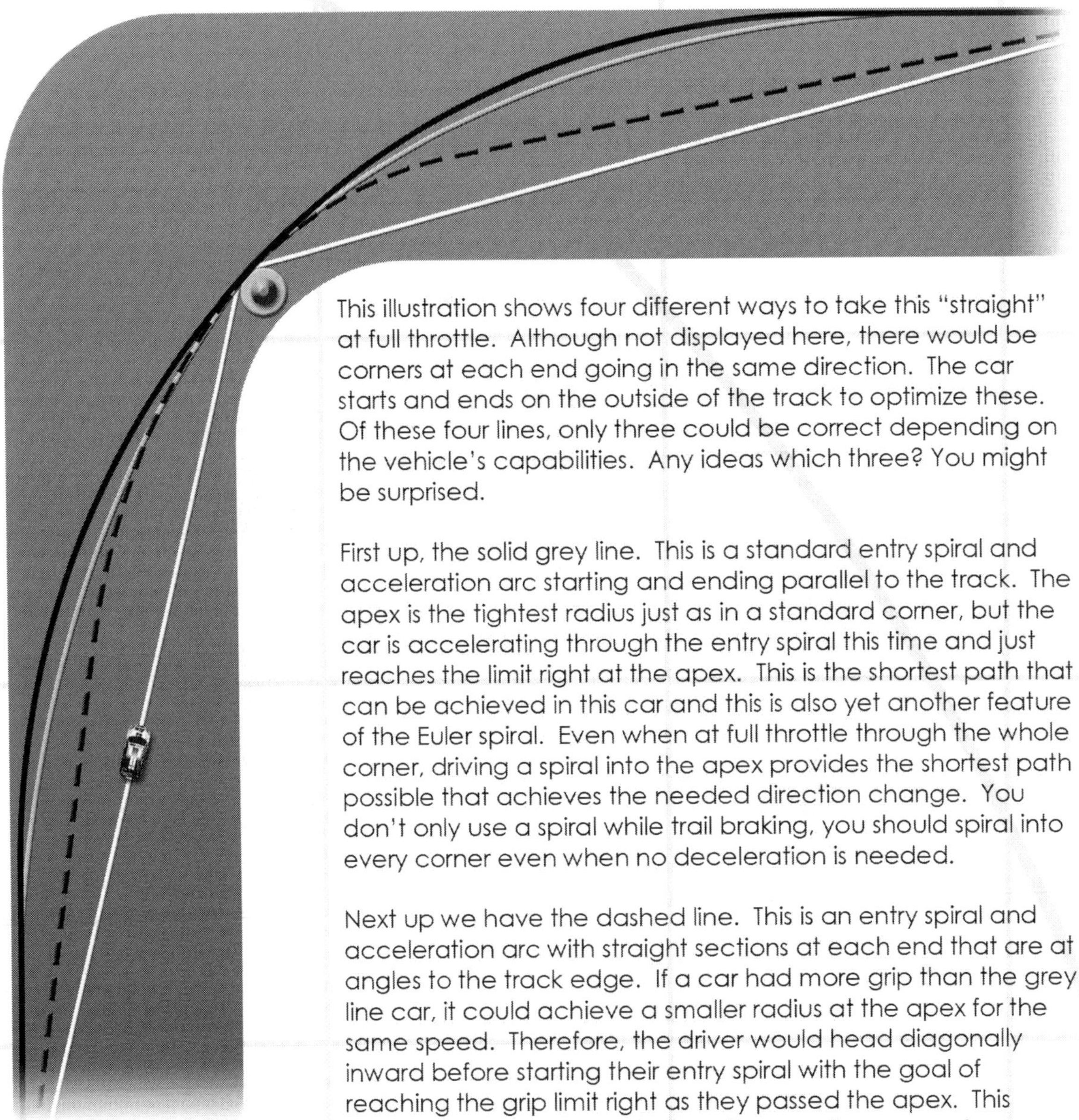

This illustration shows four different ways to take this "straight" at full throttle. Although not displayed here, there would be corners at each end going in the same direction. The car starts and ends on the outside of the track to optimize these. Of these four lines, only three could be correct depending on the vehicle's capabilities. Any ideas which three? You might be surprised.

First up, the solid grey line. This is a standard entry spiral and acceleration arc starting and ending parallel to the track. The apex is the tightest radius just as in a standard corner, but the car is accelerating through the entry spiral this time and just reaches the limit right at the apex. This is the shortest path that can be achieved in this car and this is also yet another feature of the Euler spiral. Even when at full throttle through the whole corner, driving a spiral into the apex provides the shortest path possible that achieves the needed direction change. You don't only use a spiral while trail braking, you should spiral into every corner even when no deceleration is needed.

Next up we have the dashed line. This is an entry spiral and acceleration arc with straight sections at each end that are at angles to the track edge. If a car had more grip than the grey line car, it could achieve a smaller radius at the apex for the same speed. Therefore, the driver would head diagonally inward before starting their entry spiral with the goal of reaching the grip limit right as they passed the apex. This would allow a shorter path than the grey line car and successfully follow the Full-Throttle Corner Rule*. Only two lines to go. Any ideas which could be correct and which can't?

If you had a car with a top speed of 5 mph, the shortest path achievable would be to drive straight to the apex and then drive straight to the exit on the white line. This is the fastest line possible if the speed at which the vehicle reaches the apex is extremely low. It's hard to tell from the illustration, but this is actually the same technique as our previous two lines because although it looks just like two straight lines, there would be a little entry spiral and acceleration arc right at the apex where the car reaches the limit. Also realize that even if a car reaches the apex at a more typical speed, but the corner was a mile long, it would still drive a path like this. The scale of a corner has the same effect that vehicle performance has on the ideal full-throttle corner line. The takeaway here is that for a full-throttle corner, you want the smallest entry spiral and acceleration arc you can achieve without having to lift. This is opposed to a standard corner where you want the largest spiral and arc you can fit on the track.

> For a full-throttle corner, you want the smallest entry spiral and acceleration arc you can achieve without having to lift.

The only line that couldn't be correct is the perfectly circular dark line. Let's say the circular dark line is the tightest arc a car could achieve at its top speed. It would drive at the limit through the entire corner using full throttle. This seems like it might be ideal, but let's look closer. Do you recognize what the driver would actually be doing here? They would treating this as a standard corner, but driving a slower circular entry. Your corner entry should ideally always be a spiral, even for a "straight." To understand why, let's back up a bit and look at our spiral entries again to see why we want to reach the limit **exactly** at the apex.

REACHING THE **LIMIT** AT THE **APEX**

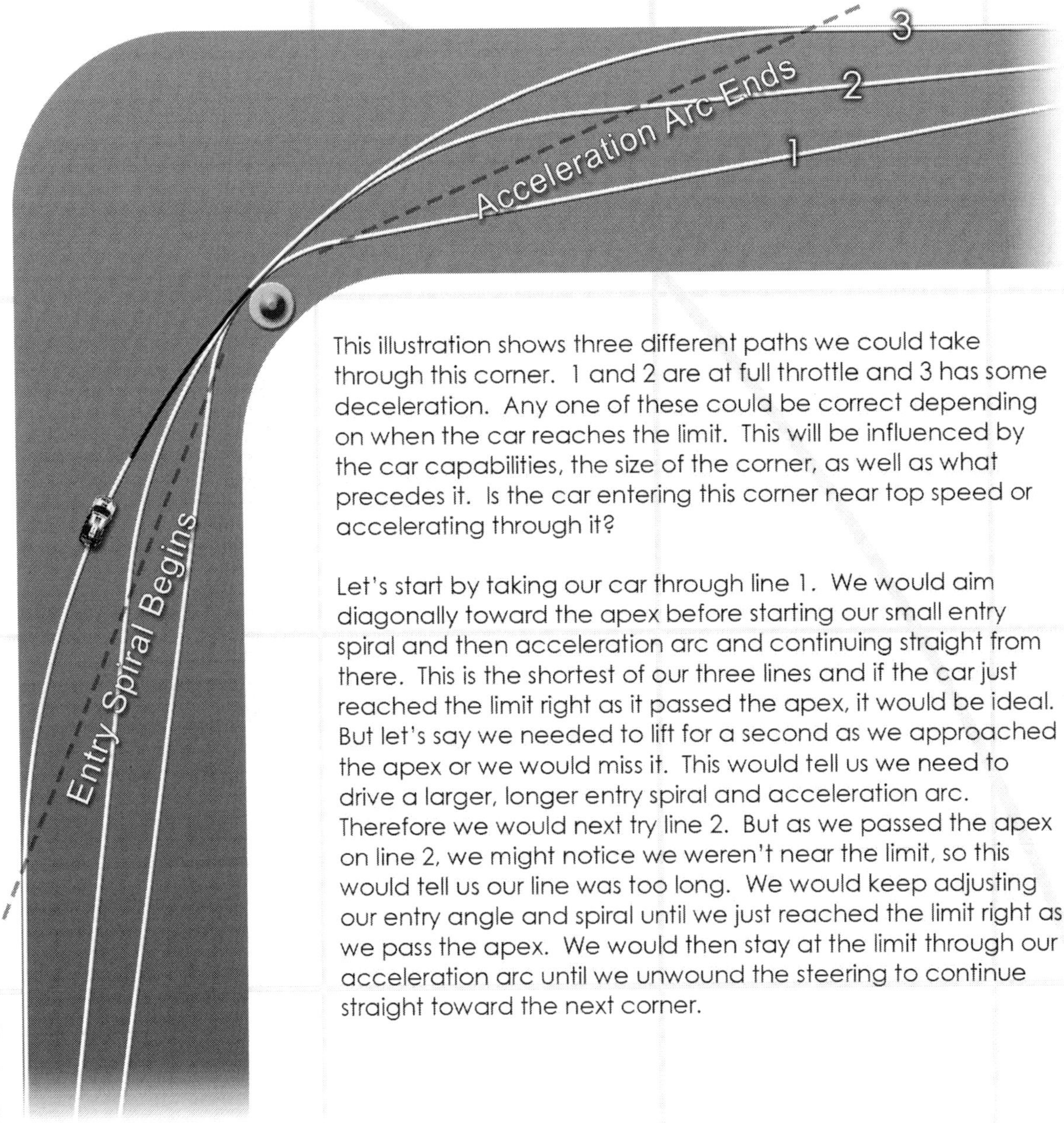

Acceleration Arc Ends

3
2
1

Entry Spiral Begins

This illustration shows three different paths we could take through this corner. 1 and 2 are at full throttle and 3 has some deceleration. Any one of these could be correct depending on when the car reaches the limit. This will be influenced by the car capabilities, the size of the corner, as well as what precedes it. Is the car entering this corner near top speed or accelerating through it?

Let's start by taking our car through line 1. We would aim diagonally toward the apex before starting our small entry spiral and then acceleration arc and continuing straight from there. This is the shortest of our three lines and if the car just reached the limit right as it passed the apex, it would be ideal. But let's say we needed to lift for a second as we approached the apex or we would miss it. This would tell us we need to drive a larger, longer entry spiral and acceleration arc. Therefore we would next try line 2. But as we passed the apex on line 2, we might notice we weren't near the limit, so this would tell us our line was too long. We would keep adjusting our entry angle and spiral until we just reached the limit right as we pass the apex. We would then stay at the limit through our acceleration arc until we unwound the steering to continue straight toward the next corner.

This all sounds pretty good, by why is this the best solution? Why don't we want to reach the limit before the apex? Why do we want to drive a straight line into a spiral shaped entry? To understand why, let's steadily dial up the entry speed in our car and continue to follow the rule to see what happens. As the speed at which we reached the apex grew, we would need to drive a bigger and bigger entry spiral until eventually we reached line 3. We would still be at full throttle the whole way through the corner, but we would have the biggest entry spiral and acceleration arc we could fit. We would reach the limit right as we pass the apex and carry the limit all the way to the edge of the track as in a standard corner.

Let's now give the car just a little bit more entry speed so it would reach the limit a car length before the apex. In order to make the apex, the driver would now need to lift for a split second before reapplying throttle at the apex. According to the Full-Throttle Corner Rule* this would tell us we need to increase the size of our entry spiral and acceleration arc yet again. We're already using as much track as possible though so we can't do that. Well what do we do then? Is our Rule* broken already? What's going on here?

What has happened is that our straight has just become a late entry spiral corner. It is no longer a full-throttle corner (a straight) and standard Line Theory rules take over. This also means there is nothing we can do to exit this corner any faster. Our apex is set as our acceleration arc already takes us to the very edge of the track. Since our apex is set, so is our entry spiral. Any extra entry speed can now only be used to reach the apex in less time, but the apex and path don't change.

Extra entry speed would continue to move the deceleration point further and further away from the apex until we reached the very beginning of the spiral. At that point, any extra entry speed now would require some threshold straight-line braking before our entry spiral. In all these situations though, the path we took, and the speeds we were at past the deceleration point would all be the same. Hopefully this gave some people an Aha! Moment, but let's go to a low-powered car that has a more circular acceleration arc to dig even deeper.

We'll redo this from the point we were on line 3 and were reaching the limit at the apex, but still using full throttle the whole way through. Unlike the high-acceleration car however, we now don't have the power to stay at the limit along the previous acceleration arc. Our acceleration arc for this car would be more circular and we wouldn't need to use the entire track at corner exit.

> What will never happen is that we will bypass the entry spiral and drive a perfectly circular arc through the corner.

Bonus points if you already figured out how to fix this, but before we cover that, let's raise the entry speed the same as before where we would hit the limit a car length before the apex. As in the high-acceleration car, the driver would need to lift to make the apex. The difference however, is that after passing the apex, the car would do the same circular acceleration arc it just did and not use up the whole corner exit. This doesn't seem right, surely this is not the fastest this car can exit the corner? It's not, and what the driver just did is a mistake we learned about from basic Line Theory.

Did you identify the mistake? We'll wait while you grab your copy of *The Perfect Corner*. This driver has just apexed too late. They should start their entry spiral a little sooner and apex earlier and faster. They would then be able to reach the apex without having to lift. This is not yet a corner however and as before, the driver will still aim to reach the limit right as they pass the apex. If the driver continued increasing entry speed, they would eventually reach the point where their circular acceleration arc would push them to the very edge of the track. This is now the crossover point where this straight is about to become a corner and just as before, the apex and acceleration arc are now set and there is no way to exit this corner any faster. The entry spiral is also set and as we increase entry speed, the deceleration point will simply move further and further from the apex. What will never happen is that we would bypass the entry spiral and drive a circular path through the whole corner.

THE **SHORTEST** PATH POSSIBLE

Now that we've seen why you always spiral into the apex and reach the limit right as you pass it, let's talk about the other part of the Full-Throttle Corner Rule*. Taking the shortest path possible. If you haven't noticed, all the lines we've shown so far are balanced right on the apex. The entry spiral and acceleration arc are similar in size. This is not an accident and it's important to keep in mind. In standard corners this will happen automatically as you optimize for the edge of the track, but in full-throttle corners you are essentially creating your own track edges so you will have to balance the entry and exit yourself.

This illustration shows two lines that both spiral into and reach the limit right at the apex. Line 2 however, is longer and would take more time to travel along. It has a very early apex with a very small entry spiral and much larger acceleration arc. A line like this can be an easy trap to fall into if you don't understand how to optimize full-throttle corners as it is often a driver's instinct to maximize the track at corner exit. A driver may even go so far as to apex early enough that they have to brake before the apex. Just try to remember that the track edges only start to determine your apex once you have to lift. Before that happens, you still have a full-throttle corner and will want to try to equalize the size of your entry spiral and acceleration arc. This will provide the shortest path possible. The outside edge of the track doesn't matter yet.

THE PROBLEM WITH **INDUCED DRAG**

Now that we've wrapped this up neat and tidy we get to tell you why the Full Throttle Corner Rule* has that asterisk and why it might not be ideal in all situations. Once a driver has to lift and standard Line Theory takes over, the rules are pretty straightforward, but prior to this our little friend **induced drag** likes to cause problems. While there are all kinds of drag, basically the only one the driver has direct control over is induced drag. Induced drag acts as a braking force on the vehicle during cornering and this takes up some of the engine power that could be used to accelerate the car. If a tire produced no induced drag whatsoever we could take away that little asterisk,

Unfortunately, there is always at least some drag anytime the tire is generating lateral force, although it is typically a relatively small amount when cornering forces are low. It can rise quickly as the tire approaches the limit however. Another problem is that induced drag is not linear and can be significantly different from one car to the next. In a car with very responsive race tires with high cornering stiffness, the induced drag is going to be less, but if the car has more flexible high-profile tires, the amount of induced drag at the limit can be quite significant.

During standard corner optimization we aren't directly concerned with induced drag. We certainly don't want to create excess induced drag by steering more than necessary, but if a driver can keep the tires right at the limit, the induced drag will simply be part of what determines their ideal acceleration arc. For a full-throttle exit in a standard corner, the driver wants as much lateral force as possible and will just live with whatever drag that produces. To understand why, imagine a car going through a standard corner with a full-throttle corner exit speed of 100 mph. The amount of total drag at the limit is taking up all the power so the driver would take a circular exit to the very edge of the track going 100 mph the whole way. Again, this is a pretty realistic scenario for a lower-powered car because at these speeds, the aero drag is significant and the induced drag from the tires will only add to that making acceleration very difficult.

Now let's see if we can reduce the induced drag to use some of that power it's taking up so we can accelerate during the corner exit. We'll try apexing at only 95 mph and not go the very limit of the tires to minimize the drag. We'll be going slower at the apex, but now we can accelerate. As we pass the apex we start to pick up speed, but we're careful not to go too close to the limit because we don't want to increase our induced drag. We complete the corner and see that reducing drag allowed us to successfully accomplish our goal of accelerating. We were able to reach 98 mph by the trackout point! All joking aside, it should be pretty intuitive that this is slower than optimum, but then what is so different about a full-throttle corner that might cause us to want to drive below the limit to reduce drag?

The primary differences are that our apex speed is already set and also that we aren't using the entire track at corner exit. When we approach a full-throttle corner, our apex speed is determined by the speed we are able to accelerate to by the point we reach the apex. According to the Full-Throttle Corner Rule* we would drive the shortest path possible that would have us reach the limit right at the apex. The higher the speed we can attain, the larger the entry spiral will need to be to not exceed the limit.

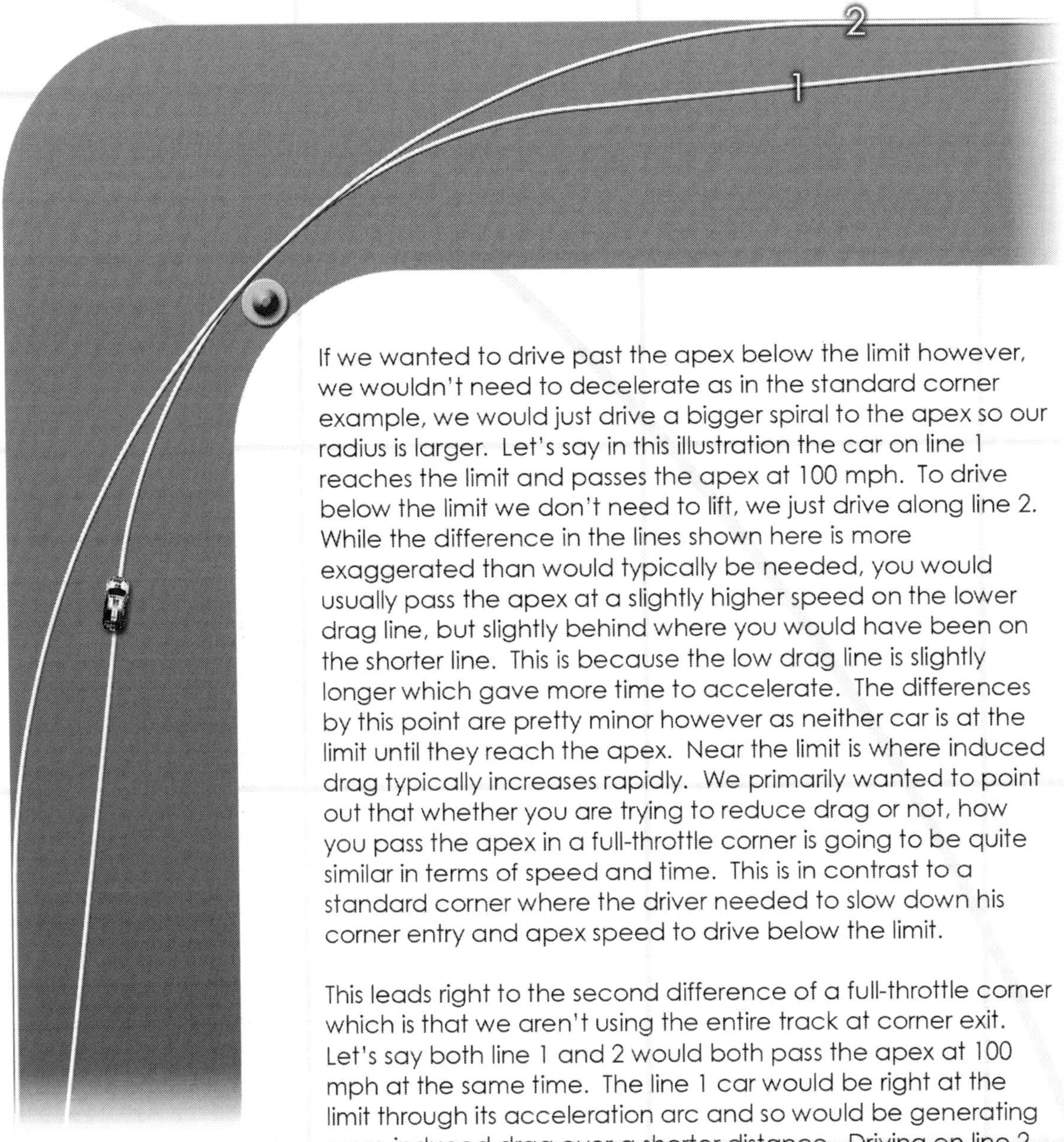

If we wanted to drive past the apex below the limit however, we wouldn't need to decelerate as in the standard corner example, we would just drive a bigger spiral to the apex so our radius is larger. Let's say in this illustration the car on line 1 reaches the limit and passes the apex at 100 mph. To drive below the limit we don't need to lift, we just drive along line 2. While the difference in the lines shown here is more exaggerated than would typically be needed, you would usually pass the apex at a slightly higher speed on the lower drag line, but slightly behind where you would have been on the shorter line. This is because the low drag line is slightly longer which gave more time to accelerate. The differences by this point are pretty minor however as neither car is at the limit until they reach the apex. Near the limit is where induced drag typically increases rapidly. We primarily wanted to point out that whether you are trying to reduce drag or not, how you pass the apex in a full-throttle corner is going to be quite similar in terms of speed and time. This is in contrast to a standard corner where the driver needed to slow down his corner entry and apex speed to drive below the limit.

This leads right to the second difference of a full-throttle corner which is that we aren't using the entire track at corner exit. Let's say both line 1 and 2 would both pass the apex at 100 mph at the same time. The line 1 car would be right at the limit through its acceleration arc and so would be generating more induced drag over a shorter distance. Driving on line 2 would have less drag, but is a longer path. So which is faster?

We have no idea. While driving the shortest line should theoretically be faster, if the amount of drag on the car rises significantly as it nears the limit, a longer line further from the limit with less drag might be faster. We wish we could offer a more concrete answer here, but fine-tuned Universal Cue sensitivity, some trial and error, and a stop watch will probably be required to figure out the optimum for each different car and full-throttle corner.

In general however, we recommend trying to keep the tires near the lower side of the transitional grip area. This provides the greatest force in relation to the amount of drag produced. A sensitive driver will be able to feel they have reached the transitional area as the turning rate will begin to taper off with extra steering input as the car approaches the limit. A stiffer race tire will typically have a smaller transitional area closer to the peak. More flexible tires will have a longer, more rounded transitional area.

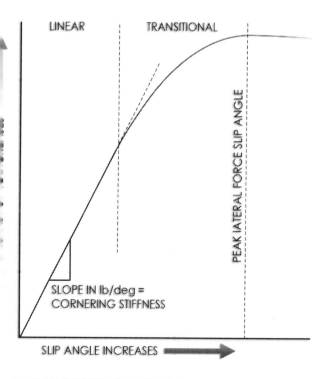

Staying closer to the linear region will provide a good balance between distance and drag. In reality, for most race tires, the difference in lines between the limit and the lower end of the transitional area will be much closer together than shown in our example illustration.

You will probably also want to minimize testing with the steering wheel and err on the side of reduced drag, at least in a race situation. This also shows us how we might want to correct a standard corner exit when we've apexed too slow. If the car is not forcing us to use the whole track, we might want to go ahead and use more of it anyway to reduce drag. How much will of course depend on the tires, but also which way we need to go next.

CHOOSE YOUR PATH

While the full-throttle corner does provide a challenge in terms of balancing drag and distance, it does have a benefit as well. It allows us to choose the corner exit ideal direction at any point during the exit. During a full-throttle corner exit, a driver should try to keep the car at the understeer limit while using the whole track. So far, we have always then unwound the steering right at the track edge and our ideal direction would be parallel to that.

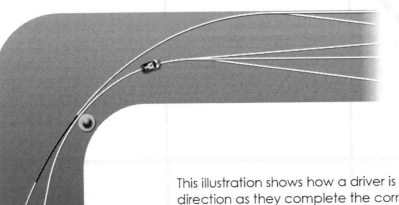

If we wanted to however, we could continue turning and angle our ideal direction inward if we wished. Up to the 90-degree limit anyway. As we saw earlier, you should ideally aim your exit directly at the next corner entry to minimize the distance traveled.

This illustration shows how a driver is able to choose their ideal direction as they complete the corner. They will simply unwind in the direction they wish to go and this becomes their ideal direction. This works the same for a fully optimized standard corner driven at the limit or when not using the whole track in a full-throttle corner.

This only works for a full-throttle corner exit however. When the car is capable of wheelspin during corner exit and you can't use full throttle, you need to set your ideal direction before you pass the apex as this shows you how to trade steering for throttle. Fortunately, we don't have to worry about that here. Even a very powerful car will be at full throttle in a... full-throttle corner.

CONNECTING **FULL-THROTTLE CORNERS**

The reason a driver might want to choose something other than following the edge of the track all comes down to what follows the corner. This illustration below shows how a driver may want to exit toward the outside of the track for two completely different reasons. In both scenarios, the driver is coming out of a full-throttle corner and will exit the acceleration arc at the same angle.

Line 1 will then continue straight toward the entry of a standard corner beginning with straight-line braking. The second corner is not full-throttle so they will want to fit the largest entry spiral they can. Therefore, as soon as the acceleration arc from the first corner is angled toward the spiral starting point, they will unwind and drive straight toward it. The dashed line then shows where the driver is going straight and ideally wants the shortest path possible. While line 1 shows this ideal solution, the driver may wish to do a larger acceleration arc and move to the edge of the track. This will reduce drag and make setting up the second corner easier

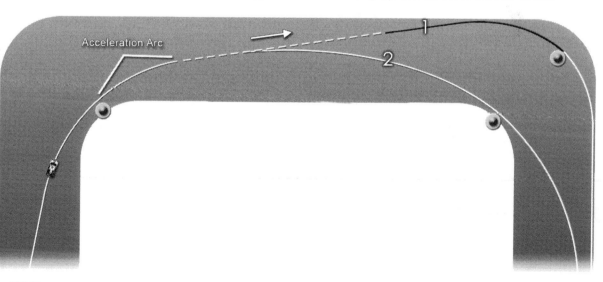

Acceleration Arc

with a parallel entry. Whether or not you should reduce drag through a full-throttle corner will depend not only on the tires, but also on what follows. Reducing drag at least somewhat for line 1 is most likely a good idea. Opening up our acceleration arc will have only a minimal effect on the travel distance and also helps in setting up the entry spiral to the second corner. As we'll see shortly, reducing drag through a full-throttle corner is not always so obviously beneficial.

Line 2 shows the unique challenge that comes with optimizing two full-throttle corners in a row. The driver will need to determine what size spirals and arcs they need to reach the limit right at each apex while also trying to equalize their size. Not only this, but the driver will need to worry about possible drag reduction. Driving at the limit can be somewhat simpler in that it removes choices. But here, once the driver leaves the first acceleration arc, they have a big wide-open track and they won't be at the limit until they reach the next apex. It will often be tempting to just drive a big circular arc or head straight toward the second corner and apex it too early. Neither of these is the best answer however. The driver has exited the first corner at this specific angle only because that is the exact spiral starting angle they will need when they reach the exact point they start turning so they arrive at the second apex right as they reach the limit and then drive an equal size acceleration arc out. I bet you never knew driving a "straight" could be so complicated.

Luckily, there are very few corners like this out there and unless you are way off the optimum, the time difference of just doing a big arc will be minor. Working through exercises like this can really help to solidify your understanding of the physics of racing however. Plus, if you put in the effort to understand it, when you do come out of a full-throttle corner with another big open corner in front of you, you'll know exactly what to do.

So before we move on, let's do a quick test to see if you remember the rules. Assuming the driver is properly reaching the limit at each apex, which of these lines below could be correct?

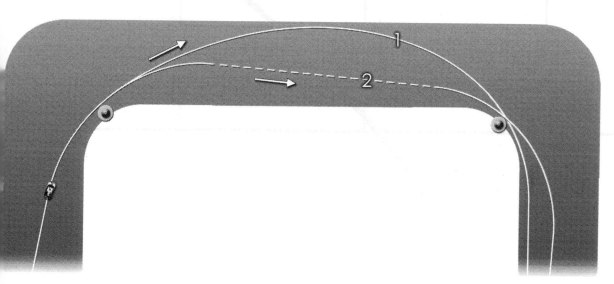

The answer is line 2. The second corner of line 1 is very unbalanced with a small acceleration arc in comparison to the giant entry spiral that started right at the first corner's acceleration arc. This created an unnecessarily long line. Line 2 shows how the line would look if the car were near top speed through the first turn and wasn't accelerating much. The driver would then drive straight and continue at top speed through the second corner equalizing the entries and exits.

However, what if the car was accelerating hard through the first turn, still reaching the limit at the apex, but would never complete line 2 without having to lift? Although the 1st corner would be set, where they exited the acceleration arc would change. They would need an exit angle from the 1st corner somewhere in between line 1 and 2. This would create a larger **equal size** entry spiral and acceleration arc through the second corner so that they would reach the limit right at the apex.

OPPOSING **FULL-THROTTLE CORNERS**

We're finally coming to the end of our techniques, but before we move on to some real-world examples of complex sequences let's flip our second corner and look at a few more scenarios. These corners aren't close enough together to be an official chicane, but they are also not far enough apart to separate completely by tracking out all the way.

In this scenario below, the first corner is taken at full throttle and as before, our driver can choose the direction of their corner exit. This is followed by another full throttle corner so the driver will need to find the correct exit angle to ensure the second corner has a balanced entry and exit and that they reach the limit at the apex. While this can already be quite challenging, the driver must also decide if and how much to try to reduce drag. This line in the illustration shows the ideal zero-drag solution where the driver is at the limit though both acceleration arcs.

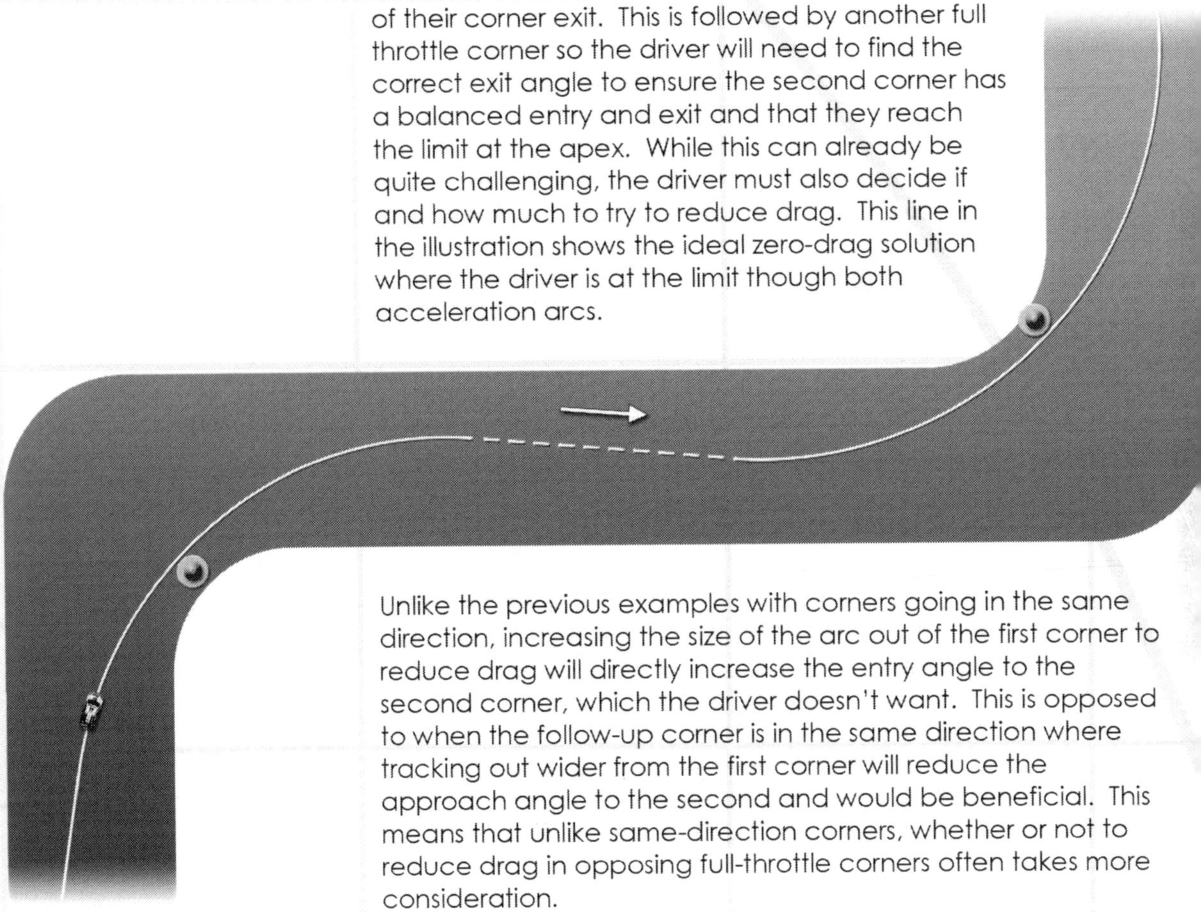

Straights

Unlike the previous examples with corners going in the same direction, increasing the size of the arc out of the first corner to reduce drag will directly increase the entry angle to the second corner, which the driver doesn't want. This is opposed to when the follow-up corner is in the same direction where tracking out wider from the first corner will reduce the approach angle to the second and would be beneficial. This means that unlike same-direction corners, whether or not to reduce drag in opposing full-throttle corners often takes more consideration.

We have some clues in this case however, that we still should probably try to reduce drag by not going to the limit. First, the corners are both full throttle and not taking up the whole track. Second, we also have a section in the middle where we are driving straight. As shown in this illustration, this will allow us to increase the entries and exits to both corners by using the extra track width as well as the straight section in the middle. This path shown now offers the minimum drag possible through this sequence and we are not at the limit anywhere. We are using the largest spirals and arcs we can fit just as we would if this was a standard chicane.

Keep in mind however that this line won't necessarily be faster. We are only trying it because the last line was driven at the limit. If we had already been at the bottom of the transitional grip area before, then this line would just be unnecessarily long. Possibly, somewhere in between these lines would be fastest depending on the car. Only testing and fine-tuned car control skills will give you the answer to how much you should reduce drag in sections such as this.

Straights

Straights

Let's now look at the one final scenario we haven't covered yet. A full-throttle corner into an opposing standard corner. This is a somewhat common scenario and can be quite tricky. See if you can figure out why this line shown in the illustration is ideal. Is the driver reducing drag anywhere? Why are they not quite using the whole track on entry to the second corner?

Did you have any ideas? There are a few sneaky things going on here so let's walk through it step-by-step. Going through the first corner, the driver would not want to reduce drag. The first reason is that as we learned in the last example, this will cause an increased angle to the second corner because it goes in the opposite direction. We don't want that here because we are already at the 90-degree limit on entry to the second corner. Just as it's hard to tell in the illustration, finding the 90-degree limit can also be difficult on track. But as we learned earlier, if the driver attempts a corner entry over 90 degrees, they will notice they need to start driving a more circular path as they approach the apex. The driver has done the tightest acceleration arc out of the first corner possible, but as soon as they reach 90 degrees from the following apex, they need to transition or they will break the 90-degree limit on that entry.

This is also why the driver has not used the entire track for their entry spiral to second corner. By the time the driver would be able to reach the very edge of the track, their entry spiral to the corner would be too circular. Sequences like this can be quite tricky so we'll look at some real world examples of similar corners in this upcoming section.

CASE STUDIES: **COMPLEX SECTIONS**

So it's been a long journey, but we've finally covered all the rules needed to tackle any type of corner with virtually any vehicle. Knowledge is only the beginning however. Now you will need to internalize and train these techniques until they become instinctual.

To begin to solidify what you've learned, it might be a good idea to find some difficult corner combinations that always gave you trouble. Try to approach them from your newfound perspective and see if you can find the chicanes, the double apexes, the late entry spirals and how these all fit together. Print out a track map, grab your imaginary cones, and go to work. Even if you aren't able to accomplish the optimum yet, see if you can work out what the optimum might be in your car. Then see if you can figure out how it would change with a different type of car.

To get you started, we are going to finish this book with several examples of complex corner sequences from around the world. Everything we have learned so far will be applicable, but we have selected some of the most difficult corner sequences out there to push your understanding of Line Theory to the limit. Gone are the days that new tracks are just standard corners and the occasional chicane. Modern track designs incorporate purposely-complex sequences that will confuse even many high-level drivers. In addition, whether on purpose or not, even many classic tracks also feature sections that confuse many drivers and we'll look at some of those as well. If you can break down and solve these puzzling sequences, you will be able to figure out how to drive anything.

REAL WORLD **DRAG REDUCTION**

This is turn 13-14 from the old Silverstone layout. See anything wrong with this chicane technique? It looks like we don't start our entry spiral until a little bit after the transition. We have also touched the near edge without quite touching the far edge first. This would usually tell us to move our imaginary cone further out and pass the 1st apex earlier and faster.

But if you've been paying attention, you'll recognize that this is actually not a chicane. It's a full-throttle corner into a late entry spiral. This sequence is preceded by only a short straight so the car was already at full throttle all the way through turn 13 and can't gain any extra speed apexing earlier. It's often a driver's instinct to want to reach the inside edge as quickly as possible after 13 to setup for 14, but is this ideal? Should we maybe open up our line and use some drag reduction through 13?

When analyzing a sequence with a full-throttle corner, it's often a good idea to first just consider the ideal and then add in drag reduction if appropriate. As we've learned, the ideal is to use the tightest possible equal size spiral and arc through 13 where we just reach the limit at the apex. We would then unwind our exit in the exact direction of the beginning of an entry spiral for 14. Since turn 14 is not full throttle, we want to fit the largest entry spiral we can so it should go all way to the edge of the track.

Now the big question is should we use drag reduction through 13? Since 14 is a standard corner, our number one priority is to fit the largest spiral in the corner entry that we can so we don't compromise the apex. That means that we must touch the inside edge in our spiral at some point. From this, we can deduce that we are able to reduce drag through 13 and open up our line until the point that we aren't able to touch the inside edge during the entry spiral to 14. We would only be allowed to not touch the near side if we were at the limit coming out of 13, but needed to start our spiral to 14 before we got to the edge. That's because then turn 13 would no longer be a full-throttle corner and this sequence becomes a chicane.

A driver doesn't need to overdo the drag reduction with an unnecessarily large arc however. A low-acceleration car might stay quite close to the inside of 13 even at the bottom of the transitional grip area. This would give them a relatively long straight period before needing to start their entry spiral for 14. If the driver could move over parallel to the inside of the track during this straight with only minimal steering then that's perfectly fine. This will make setting up 14 easier and only marginally change the distance traveled.

The takeaway here is that at least some drag reduction through a full-throttle corner is okay as long as it doesn't compromise the following corner. This could be if the next corner is also full-throttle as we saw earlier or if you can still reach the edge of the track and maximize your entry spiral to the next corner.

WORKING UP A **COMPLEX SECTION**

Another sequence that confuses many drivers is turns 2 and 3 at Lime Rock. Whenever you come upon a track section that isn't easily categorized, it's generally best to break it down into its individual components and see if you can first eliminate possibilities. That will help to let you know what rules to pay attention to and which you can ignore. We're showing the finished product here in the illustration, but let's see how a driver would work through it.

First off, we can notice that there are no full-throttle corners. You aren't going to make it through any corner here without having to lift. That eliminates having to worry about drag reduction so let's go ahead and look at the first corner. We know that it's either a standard corner or the beginning of a chicane. Normally it is obvious which it is, but not here. In order to find out which, we would first try to fully optimize the

exit to the edge of the track and then continue our acceleration arc inward to the near edge of the track as if we are setting up for another corner. If we need to brake before reaching the near edge to make the next corner, we know we have a chicane. In this case, we don't have to start braking until much later, so we know that the first corner is standard and we should fully optimize it to the edge of the track. Only the Chicane Rule would have us not use the whole track at corner exit. Therefore, the first corner is now set and we can continue optimizing from here.

Next up, we have an opposing corner. With an opposing corner, we know we should ideally drive a straight line from the first corner exit to the beginning of the entry spiral and we also want the entry spiral to be as large as possible. This entry is quite difficult because it's really long and the shape of the track makes it so you won't be touching the outside. It's often a driver's instinct to want to reach the edge of the track, but that would make the entry too circular here.

When working up a really large late entry spiral like this, there are a few things you can look for to make sure you are on the right track. First off, since this is not a chicane, there is no quick transition as you enter the spiral. You won't reach the limit until much closer to the apex. Driving below the limit can feel slow so it's often a driver's instinct to want to move across the track quickly and get to the limit early. Remember however, that will create a slower, more circular entry. Driving a spiral will allow us to get as close as possible to the apex before we reach the limit, so focusing on trying to reach the highest speed you can achieve before needing to brake can be useful. You can also pay attention to your steering movement. There should be a steady progression in steering from the entry of the spiral to the apex. You shouldn't need to hold constant steering or have a quick increase in steering at any point up until the apex.

This entry is definitely going to be difficult for most drivers to optimize, but then to make this section even more fun, all this is followed by a chicane. So now, let's see how a driver can go about linking multiple track elements together.

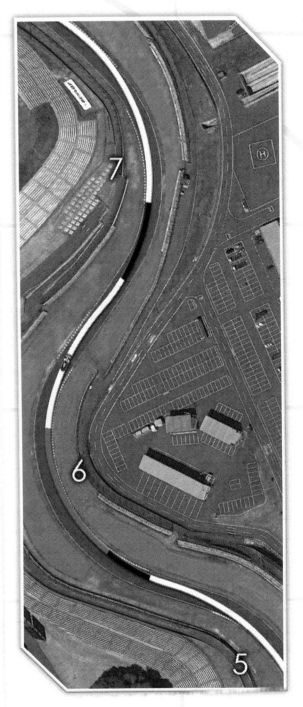

LINKING **CHICANES**

This is the esses at Suzuka. This sequence actually features four chicanes in a row, but we are only showing the last three corners where we will need to optimize two in a row. Optimizing two chicanes in a row is the same as optimizing ten.

There are no new rules for putting together complex sequences as they follow the same ones that the individual elements follow. You will want to travel the shortest path through the whole sequence you can drive on the limit that allows an optimal entry and exit. Since there are no full-throttle corners here, this means that everything in between the very first corner entry and the final exit is about efficiently staying at the limit. As before, let's start at the beginning and work our way through this.

How you exit turn 5 is set by the previous chicane, and as with all exits, we can either exit faster and earlier or slower and later. We're showing the optimum in the illustration, but there would be telltale signs if we were too fast or too slow. Just as in a single chicane, if we apexed too late and slow, we would not have to slow down until somewhat after our transition was over on the way to 6. If we apexed too early however, and continued at maximum acceleration through the transition, we would miss the apex at 6. We would need to brake before the transition ended to make it to the apex and this would tell us to apex later and slower,

There is actually a fairly small window of apex angles that you will have to work with that will still satisfy the Chicane Rule. Following the rule, you will either end up at turn 6 with a faster and earlier apex or a later and slower one just as you did at 5. You then use the Chicane Rule again on this next chicane into 7 to find out where your turn 6 apex should be. If it needed to be earlier or later you would then need to go back to turn 5 and adjust that one as it directly affects how you pass 6. All the apexes of multiple chicanes in a row are connected.

> Theoretically, how you hit the very first chicane will determine how you come out of the very last one.

You will need to optimize each in turn while going back and adjusting the previous ones as necessary. This can take a while to optimize if you have a long sequence of chicanes because theoretically how you hit the very first chicane will determine how you come out of the very last one. Realistically however, you're never going to link one chicane to the next perfectly and are going to be making corrections throughout. Being able to understand how one chicane's apex affects the next will help guide you in the process however.

The Suzuka esses are somewhat unique however, and have an interesting feature that can help us. As we make it to turn 6, we can't start accelerating as soon as we hit the apex. We'll need to use the Double Apex Rule and stay near the inside of the turn (at the limit) until we can begin accelerating again for the chicane into 7.

Remember, narrow tracks and long turns have a tendency to create double apexes. Adding in chicanes effectively makes the track even narrower so while we are only showing the double apex portion in 6 since it's quite long, you would probably be using the Double Apex Rule for at least a few feet at each apex. This will especially be true for higher acceleration cars that have a faster opening acceleration arc and need a later apex.

Another nice thing about needing to use the Double Apex Rule on a curve like turn 6 is that it effectively resets any mistakes you've made. It unlinks the chicanes. Many double apexes are more squared off and have two distinct apex points where the angle you pass one directly affects the next. Sometimes however, as in turn 6 or when you double apex a hairpin, the inner portion of the track is rounded and you will simply follow along the inside just as you would in the circular racetrack example. Turn 6 is like this in that you will just follow the inside of the track staying at the limit until you reach the angle you need to accelerate for the next corner. You would have to make a serious error going into 6 to not be able to reach the limit on the inside of the track by the point you needed to accelerate into the final chicane.

Resetting any mistakes in turn 6 is quite nice because the final chicane is very important to hit correctly from a lap time perspective as it leads into a long straight. Simply staying along the inside of the track at the limit through 6 actually makes this easier to optimize than a standard chicane as you just need to worry about your acceleration point and not optimizing an entry spiral to set your angle. While the other corners in the esses are not as long as 6, you will probably have at least a little time at each apex to fix your mistakes as well. Make sure you don't overdue this however. Finding a single apex to optimize is going to be faster if one is available.

Overall, the Suzuka esses are not that complicated if you understand how one chicane affects the next. There really isn't anything overly complex about it, but it has many linked elements and might take many laps before you have them all optimized.

SUZUKA
INTERNATIONAL RACING COURSE

SHORT **CHICANES** TO **90-DEGREE EXIT**

The downhill chicanes at Barber Motorsports Park can be quite confusing to optimize and will fool many drivers with a few tricky parts. What's hard to tell from the photo is that there is a significant elevation drop from turn 7 to 9. This makes this sequence difficult because cars need to lose a good deal of speed and the chicanes don't quite allow a straight shot through them. They need a little bit of steering to negotiate.

What many drivers will do is use the brakes the whole time as they steer through this sequence, but remember you should never brake past an apex unless you are in a double apex. In fact, theoretically, you should be accelerating hard after each apex. You certainly wouldn't have time here to go hard on the throttle during the short acceleration areas, but you want to aim to at least be off the brakes as you pass each apex. Following the Chicane Rule, you want to make sure you don't get back on the brakes until you have the steering wheel turned back toward the next apex. The straighter you can make this chicane by using the curbs more effectively, the quicker you'll be able to get the steering turned in the right direction to use the brakes.

It is really important that you follow the Chicane Rule here because, although it may feel fast to just brake down the whole hill, this can compromise your exit from turn 9. The main problem with carrying too much speed into 7 and having to brake the whole way down would be how it affects your apex angle through each corner. If you hit turn 7 too early and fast you will then hit 8 and 9 too early and fast. Remember one chicane affects the next one and there is no long corner like at Suzuka to reset any mistakes. These corners are very close together so you won't be able to do much correction to minimize your first error.

In addition, if you apex turn 9 too early and fast, you can really hurt your lap times since the exit will go more than 90 degrees and you will start canceling out tire forces. Turn 9 leads to a long straight so you definitely don't want to compromise the apex. This can be quite tricky especially for lower-acceleration cars because it's a long curved exit and even if done correctly, you will be right at the 90-degree limit. It's easy to go over and not realize it. You might need to use the Double Apex Rule for a bit as you delay going to the throttle coming out of 9.

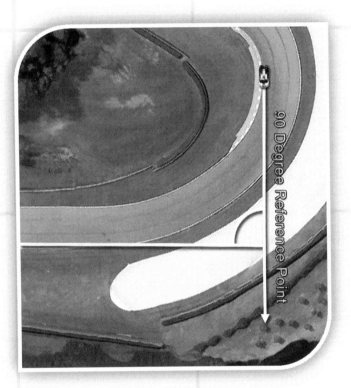

90 Degree Reference Point

It is also often more difficult finding the 90-degree limit during a corner exit than during corner entry. During corner entry, you typically start right at the edge of the track so you know the ideal direction will be at that same angle and if you go over 90 degrees your path will become more circular as you approach the apex. During a full-throttle corner exit however, your path will be very circular anyway and you also won't know the ideal direction until you see the trackout point.

In really large corners such as this, you often can't even see the track out point until you are a good distance into your exit. It might be beneficial to find an overhead photo of the track to locate the exact angle at the apex of the 90-degree limit. You could even find a reference point along this line that will let you know you shouldn't leave the inside of the track until the angle of the car has passed it. Also, take into account that you might not always want your final exit to end up exactly parallel to the track. Sometimes you might want to aim your exit inward somewhat depending on the next corner, so adjust your 90-degree limit accordingly.

EXPANDING **DOUBLE APEX** TO **90-DEGREE EXIT**

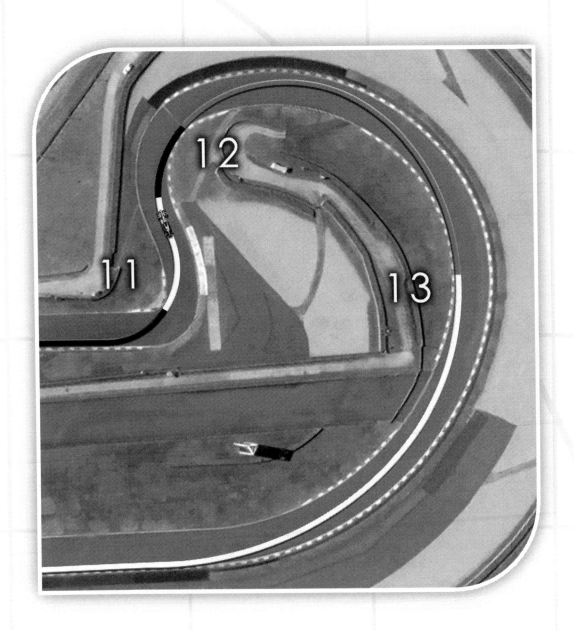

The next corner sequence we will look at is at the Shanghai International Circuit. Hermann Tilke must have woken up on the wrong side of the bed the day he started designing this track. If you're anything like us however, and enjoy the challenge of breaking down complex sections, then look no further. Turns 11-13 is interesting because it incorporates not only a large exit where you must pay attention to the 90-degree limit, but also the rare increasing-radius double apex. This is similar to the Road Atlanta Short connecting corner we looked at earlier, but is even more complex.

Turn 11 to 12 is a pretty standard chicane, but it leads into almost 270 degrees of constant acceleration, which is well beyond the 90-degree limit so we will definitely need the Double Apex Rule. In order to stay under this limit, a driver will need to have a 2nd apex at a point no more than 90 degrees before the following straightaway. The driver will therefore need to find just the right 1st apex angle and acceleration in the double apex portion that allows them to stay at the limit as long as possible without needing a speed reversal, but also without breaking the final 90-degree limit. This is obviously not easy.

Depending on the car, this can end up looking quite different. The line in our illustration depicts a high-acceleration F1 car where the double apex usually won't be done under full acceleration the entire way, but it will be fairly close. The 2nd apex will need to be right at 90 degrees from the exit because an F1 car has the power to track out all the way from that point, but just barely. If they leave the track edge sooner, they break the 90-degree rule and cancel out tire forces, but if they apex a little later they won't be maximizing their exit.

For the double apex portion, it looks like a car might want to just stay along the inside of the track between 12-13 as it is quite rounded similar to Suzuka turn 6. A car needs so much speed coming out of 13 however, that even an F1 car will need to generate more speed than staying along the inside of the curb would allow. If a driver apexed later and slower out of 12 and tried to stay closer to the inside of the track on a shorter line, they wouldn't have the speed and angle to do an optimal corner exit after 13. Remember, we want the shortest double apex line that **also** allows an optimal entry and exit. While many times the 2nd apex is set by a squared off portion of the corner, in this case, it's set by the 90 degree limit at corner exit.

How this will end up looking for a low-acceleration car will be quite different however. If a vehicle comes out of 12 at full throttle and doesn't have the acceleration potential to push out from the inside during the final corner exit, then the 2nd apex becomes a full-throttle corner (a straight). Just as in the Road Atlanta connecting corner, this will effectively change where the straight begins.

The driver will aim to have the earliest, fastest exit from the 1st apex that will allow them to stay at the limit until they reach the inside of the track. They also must not compromise their

2nd apex angle as they reach the inside of the track however. Remember that if the 1st apex is earlier and faster, the 2nd apex will be later. If the 2nd apex is too late, as in Line 2 here, the driver will end up heading directly for the inside of the track if they stay at the limit. They would need to unwind and drop below the limit to meet up with the track edge. This makes their line unnecessarily long and inefficient. Staying at the limit through a double apex is very important if you wish to take advantage of its efficiency.

As shown in line 1, a driver in a low-acceleration car would need to exit the 1st apex even later than an F1 car so their 2nd apex angle will be early enough when they soon meet up with the inside of the track. The driver will then continue this full-throttle corner all the way around.

SHANGHAI
INTERNATIONAL CIRCUIT

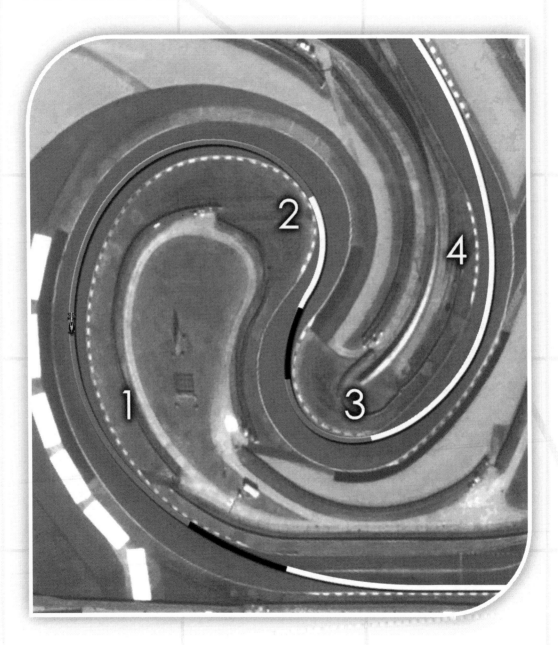

Now we're really putting our knowledge to the test. Again at Shanghai International Circuit, the first section is one of the most complex sequences in the world and we'll need to use virtually everything we have learned so far to get through it correctly.

Going into turn 1, even very powerful cars often carry full throttle into their entry spiral because even though this follows a long straight, the entry to turn 1 is very high speed. Then we get to the first tricky part of this sequence, which is from turn 1 to turn 2. This has over 180 degrees of direction change and the car will need to lose significant speed and radius through this decreasing radius double apex. Many drivers will often track out unnecessarily far through this section, but you will want to stay as close to the inside of the track as possible without needing a speed reversal. It looks like you might want to actually stay right against the inside curbing the whole way, but there are two reasons you probably wouldn't.

First, and this is true for any double apex, is that it is very important that you stay at the limit to maximize your efficiency. If you are right up against the inside of the track however, it is quite difficult to do any testing with the steering. If you were going too slow and were under the limit, but steering more to test would take you off the inside of the track, you wouldn't have any way of knowing. So when you are driving through a double apex near the inside of the track, it's generally a good idea to not stay right up against the edge. You might want to give yourself a couple feet to ensure you can stay at the limit even if this makes the line slightly longer.

The second reason is harder to tell until you try the corner a few times. While it looks you could just follow the track edge around, there is just too much radius change as you approach turn 2. Sometimes the track edge already has a constant or smoothly changing radius and we can follow right along, but that won't work here, as the radius change is not consistent. This can be hard to tell by looking at a track map, but you will quickly discover it once you try it in the car.

Turn 2 is also quite tight and trying to stay right along the edge on the approach would most likely give you too low of an apex speed going into the chicane. You do want to stay as close to the inside edge as you feasibly can however. The line shown in the illustration is a constantly decreasing radius that will have a good entry angle and speed into the chicane, but isn't unnecessarily long.

Next up, we have a chicane that leads into over 180 degrees of acceleration through some red herring track edges. Because of the large direction change, we will need a double apex section in turn 3 until we reach the 90-degree limit from our final track out point. Even though many drivers try, you aren't going to be able to get enough angle coming out of the chicane to bring the corner under 180 degrees and have one apex. A common mistake is going too early and fast into turn 3 and breaking the 90-degree limit on exit. It's generally pretty easy to spot when this happens, as the driver will be unable to start feeding in power until after they have passed their attempted single apex by a good amount. A double apex will always be needed with this large of a direction change.

While high-acceleration cars will often be able to optimize for the track edge out past turn 4, many slower cars will not have the power to track out all the way. Don't make the mistake of taking an early apex out of turn 3 and optimizing for the outside curbing after 3. It's definitely a red herring and no car would ideally go out there. This would make your exit a good bit past 90 degrees and your line unnecessarily long as you are pushed to the outside of the track all the way past 4. In lower-acceleration cars, you might also sometimes get close to the inside curbing at 4 which will then make that a full-throttle corner.

This track will really test your spatial awareness as well as your knowledge of late entry spirals, long double apexes, chicanes, the 90-degree limit, and full-throttle corners. It's a great training opportunity, but don't worry if you aren't on an F1 team. There are good versions of this track in a few sim-racing titles so you can try mastering it for yourself.

Working up new tracks sections can help you to test and solidify your knowledge, but don't limit yourself to just road courses. You can look at the many different types of motorsport to see how the physics of racing can work anywhere. Watch how superspeedway racers will use the Double Apex Rule through the high-banked turns. Watch how dirt bike racers look for the grip generating ruts. See if you can figure out why rally racers use Scandinavian flicks and high slip angles. Try to find other examples of your own. There are plenty.

If this is your first read-through, you might be feeling pretty overwhelmed right now. We don't expect a driver to be able to absorb everything the first or even second and third time through. While the rules of Line Theory are pretty straight forward, figuring out how to apply them to new track sections can be quite the mental workout sometimes. There is no need to jump straight into complex sequences if you aren't ready. We recommend you start simply and work your way up. Take it one corner and one page at a time.

We wish we could just tell you to be smooth and don't miss the apex, but if it were that simple, where would the fun be? Although the road to true understanding is not always easy, if you love motorsport as much as we do, the destination is definitely worth the journey. It's quite a powerful feeling to know exactly what you should be doing at every instant on track - and not just what, but why. Not because someone told you so, but because you truly understand it yourself. For while none of us will ever quite reach it in reality, in our minds, every single one of us can drive... THE

PERFECT

CORNER.

Other Motorsport Education Titles by
PARADIGM SHIFT DRIVER DEVELOPMENT

THE PERFECT CORNER

A Driver's Step-by-Step Guide to Finding Their Own Optimal Line Through the Physics of Racing

- We will take you through an intuitive and fun lesson in the physics of racing and then we'll apply it as you learn to optimize your driving technique.

- We will look at real-world racetracks and provide an exact procedure to find the ideal approach all from the driver's-eye point of view.

- Regardless of your current level of driving experience, you can apply these methods today and remove any doubt about what you should be doing on track for good.

PERFECT CONTROL

A Driver's Step-by-Step Guide to Advanced Car Control Through the Physics of Racing

- Do you understand the true meaning of driving at the limit? Learn how to identify and prioritize the different visual, auditory, and tactile car control cues, plus the optimal driver inputs needed to extract %100 from practically any vehicle.

- We will also look in-depth at the Universal Cue. The driving cue that directly represents the physics of racing and provides the final layer of car control precision. Learn how world-class drivers use it to self-evaluate and perfect their on track performance.

These titles are available wherever quality books are sold or by visiting us at www.paradigmshiftracing.com

PARADIGM·SHIFT
DRIVER DEVELOPMENT

Made in the USA
Middletown, DE
13 March 2019